×SQA

201 ~~the library~~ IN EAST AYRSHIRE ...pers
with ...swers

# Advanced Higher
# PHYSICS

2015 Specimen Question Paper,
2016 & 2017 Exams

Hodder Gibson Study Skills Advice – General      – page 3
Hodder Gibson Study Skills Advice –
   Advanced Higher Physics      – page 5
2015 SPECIMEN QUESTION PAPER      – page 9
2016 EXAM      – page 45
2017 EXAM      – page 97
ANSWERS      – page 153

HODDER
GIBSON
AN HACHETTE UK COMPANY

This book contains the official 2015 SQA Specimen Question Paper and 2016 and 2017 Exams for Advanced Higher Physics, with associated SQA-approved answers modified from the official marking instructions that accompany the paper.

In addition the book contains study skills advice. This advice has been specially commissioned by Hodder Gibson, and has been written by experienced senior teachers and examiners in line with the Advanced Higher for CfE syllabus and assessment outlines. This is not SQA material but has been devised to provide further guidance for Advanced Higher examinations.

Hodder Gibson is grateful to the copyright holders for permission to use their material. Every effort has been made to trace the copyright holders and to obtain their permission for the use of copyright material. Hodder Gibson will be happy to receive information allowing us to rectify any error or omission in future editions.

Permission has been sought from all relevant copyright holders and Hodder Gibson is grateful for the use of the following:

Image © Calvin Chan/Shutterstock.com (2016 page 3);
Image © Diego Barbieri/Shutterstock.com (2017 page 3);
Image © Vasca/stock.adobe.com (2017 page 34).

Hachette UK's policy is to use papers that are natural, renewable and recyclable products and made from wood grown in sustainable forests. The logging and manufacturing processes are expected to conform to the environmental regulations of the country of origin.

Orders: please contact Bookpoint Ltd, 130 Park Drive, Milton Park, Abingdon, Oxon OX14 4SE. Telephone: (44) 01235 827720. Fax: (44) 01235 400454. Lines are open 9.00–5.00, Monday to Saturday, with a 24-hour message answering service. Visit our website at www.hoddereducation.co.uk. Hodder Gibson can be contacted direct on: Tel: 0141 333 4650; Fax: 0141 404 8188; email: hoddergibson@hodder.co.uk

This collection first published in 2017 by
Hodder Gibson, an imprint of Hodder Education,
An Hachette UK Company
211 St Vincent Street
Glasgow G2 5QY

Typeset by Aptara, Inc.

Printed in the UK

A catalogue record for this title is available from the British Library

ISBN: 978-1-5104-2137-0

2 1

2018 2017

# Introduction

## Study Skills – what you need to know to pass exams!

### Pause for thought

Many students might skip quickly through a page like this. After all, we all know how to revise. Do you really though?

### Think about this:

"IF YOU ALWAYS DO WHAT YOU ALWAYS DO, YOU WILL ALWAYS GET WHAT YOU HAVE ALWAYS GOT."

Do you like the grades you get? Do you want to do better? If you get full marks in your assessment, then that's great! Change nothing! This section is just to help you get that little bit better than you already are.

There are two main parts to the advice on offer here. The first part highlights fairly obvious things but which are also very important. The second part makes suggestions about revision that you might not have thought about but which WILL help you.

## Part 1

DOH! It's so obvious but …

### Start revising in good time

Don't leave it until the last minute – this will make you panic.

Make a revision timetable that sets out work time AND play time.

### Sleep and eat!

Obvious really, and very helpful. Avoid arguments or stressful things too – even games that wind you up. You need to be fit, awake and focused!

### Know your place!

Make sure you know exactly **WHEN and WHERE** your exams are.

### Know your enemy!

**Make sure you know what to expect in the exam.**

How is the paper structured?

How much time is there for each question?

What types of question are involved?

Which topics seem to come up time and time again?

Which topics are your strongest and which are your weakest?

Are all topics compulsory or are there choices?

### Learn by DOING!

There is no substitute for past papers and practice papers – they are simply essential! Tackling this collection of papers and answers is exactly the right thing to be doing as your exams approach.

## Part 2

People learn in different ways. Some like low light, some bright. Some like early morning, some like evening or night. Some prefer warm, some prefer cold. But everyone uses their BRAIN and the brain works when it is active. Passive learning – sitting gazing at notes – is the most INEFFICIENT way to learn anything. Below you will find tips and ideas for making your revision more effective and maybe even more enjoyable. What follows gets your brain active, and active learning works!

### Activity 1 – Stop and review

#### Step 1

When you have done no more than 5 minutes of revision reading STOP!

#### Step 2

Write a heading in your own words which sums up the topic you have been revising.

#### Step 3

Write a summary of what you have revised in no more than two sentences. Don't fool yourself by saying, "I know it, but I cannot put it into words". That just means you don't know it well enough. If you cannot write your summary, revise that section again, knowing that you must write a summary at the end of it. Many of you will have notebooks full of blue/black ink writing. Many of the pages will not be especially attractive or memorable so try to liven them up a bit with colour as you are reviewing and rewriting. **This is a great memory aid, and memory is the most important thing.**

## Activity 2 – Use technology!

Why should everything be written down? Have you thought about "mental" maps, diagrams, cartoons and colour to help you learn? And rather than write down notes, why not record your revision material?

What about having a text message revision session with friends? Keep in touch with them to find out how and what they are revising and share ideas and questions.

Why not make a video diary where you tell the camera what you are doing, what you think you have learned and what you still have to do? No one has to see or hear it, but the process of having to organise your thoughts in a formal way to explain something is a very important learning practice.

Be sure to make use of electronic files. You could begin to summarise your class notes. Your typing might be slow, but it will get faster and the typed notes will be easier to read than the scribbles in your class notes. Try to add different fonts and colours to make your work stand out. You can easily Google relevant pictures, cartoons and diagrams which you can copy and paste to make your work more attractive and **MEMORABLE**.

## Activity 3 – This is it. Do this and you will know lots!

### Step 1

In this task you must be very honest with yourself! Find the SQA syllabus for your subject (www.sqa.org.uk). Look at how it is broken down into main topics called MANDATORY knowledge. That means stuff you MUST know.

### Step 2

BEFORE you do ANY revision on this topic, write a list of everything that you already know about the subject. It might be quite a long list but you only need to write it once. It shows you all the information that is already in your long-term memory so you know what parts you do not need to revise!

### Step 3

Pick a chapter or section from your book or revision notes. Choose a fairly large section or a whole chapter to get the most out of this activity.

With a buddy, use Skype, Facetime, Twitter or any other communication you have, to play the game "If this is the answer, what is the question?". For example, if you are revising Geography and the answer you provide is "meander", your buddy would have to make up a question like "What is the word that describes a feature of a river where it flows slowly and bends often from side to side?".

Make up 10 "answers" based on the content of the chapter or section you are using. Give this to your buddy to solve while you solve theirs.

### Step 4

Construct a wordsearch of at least 10 × 10 squares. You can make it as big as you like but keep it realistic. Work together with a group of friends. Many apps allow you to make wordsearch puzzles online. The words and phrases can go in any direction and phrases can be split. Your puzzle must only contain facts linked to the topic you are revising. Your task is to find 10 bits of information to hide in your puzzle, but you must not repeat information that you used in Step 3. DO NOT show where the words are. Fill up empty squares with random letters. Remember to keep a note of where your answers are hidden but do not show your friends. When you have a complete puzzle, exchange it with a friend to solve each other's puzzle.

### Step 5

Now make up 10 questions (not "answers" this time) based on the same chapter used in the previous two tasks. Again, you must find NEW information that you have not yet used. Now it's getting hard to find that new information! Again, give your questions to a friend to answer.

### Step 6

As you have been doing the puzzles, your brain has been actively searching for new information. Now write a NEW LIST that contains only the new information you have discovered when doing the puzzles. Your new list is the one to look at repeatedly for short bursts over the next few days. Try to remember more and more of it without looking at it. After a few days, you should be able to add words from your second list to your first list as you increase the information in your long-term memory.

## FINALLY! Be inspired...

Make a list of different revision ideas and beside each one write **THINGS I HAVE** tried, **THINGS I WILL** try and **THINGS I MIGHT** try. Don't be scared of trying something new.

And remember – "FAIL TO PREPARE AND PREPARE TO FAIL!"

# Advanced Higher Physics

## The course

The course comprises two whole and two half units:

- Rotational Motion and Astrophysics    (1 unit)
- Quanta and Waves    (1 unit)
- Electromagnetism    (0·5 unit)
- Investigating Physics    (0·5 unit)

### Course assessment

In order to gain an award in the course, you must pass the unit assessment in each topic. The first three topics will be internally assessed by your teacher/lecturer and the evidence externally verified. The assessments will be in the form of class tests.

### Investigating Physics

The Investigating Physics unit assessment will involve you planning your experiments and taking note of your experimental readings in your record of work/diary.

Ensure this record is neat and tidy so that when you come to type your report, it is easy to decipher. Your teacher will overview and sign your record of work/diary.

**This record could be externally verified by SQA and should be submitted to your teacher along with your project write up.**

## The examination

This will last 2·5 hours and will be marked out of **140 marks** and then scaled back to **100 marks**.

### The project

The report will be submitted to SQA for marking and will be marked out of **30 marks**.

This will then be added to the examination mark giving a total out of **130 marks**.

Experimental write ups should be typed up as you progress through the course. This will build up your skills and also allow you to easily go back and correct any mistakes or take on any suggestions from your teacher.

Become confident in the use of software packages that allow you to plot graphs including error bars. Find out how to find the gradient of a straight line and its associated uncertainty – the use of Linest function in the Microsoft package. This will save you an enormous amount of time!

See the SQA website for advice to candidates in relation to the project.

Advanced Higher Physics is an excellent qualification and although it is a step above Higher, the fact that you are in the class proves you have the ability to do well. It just takes hard work and application – the danger is to have too many distractions in your sixth year. Try to choose a project that suits and **stick to deadlines**!

## Examination tips

### Mark allocation

- **4 or 5 marks** will generally involve more than one step or several points of coverage.
- **3 marks** will generally involve the use of just one equation.

### Standard 3-mark example

Calculate the acceleration of a mass of 5 kg when acted on by a resultant force of 10 N.

| Solution 1 | Solution 2 | Solution 3 |
|---|---|---|
| $F = ma$    **(1)** | $F = ma$    **(1)** | $F = ma$    **(1)** |
| $10 = 5a$    **(1)** | $a = \dfrac{m}{F} = \dfrac{5}{10}$    **(0)** | $10 = 5a$    **(1)** |
| $a = 2\,\text{ms}^{-2}$ **(1)** | $= 0{\cdot}5\,\text{ms}^{-2}$ | $a = 0{\cdot}5\,\text{ms}^{-2}$ |
| **3 marks** | **1 mark for selecting formula.** | **2 marks for selecting formula + correct substitution.** |

Do not rearrange equations in algebraic form. Select the appropriate equation, substitute the given values then rearrange the equation to obtain the required unknown. This minimises the risk of a wrong substitution.

### Use of the Data Sheet

Clearly show where you have substituted a value from the data sheet. For example, **do not** leave $\mu_0$ in an equation. You must show the substitution $4\pi \times 10^{-7}$ in your equation.

When rounding, **do not** round the given values. For example, the mass of a proton = $1{\cdot}673 \times 10^{-27}$ kg **not** $1{\cdot}67 \times 10^{-27}$ kg.

### Use of the Physics Relationship Sheet

Although many of the required equations are given, it is better to know the basic equations to gain time in the examination.

### "Show" questions

Generally **all steps** for these must be given, even though they might seem obvious. **Do not assume that substitutions are obvious to the marker.**

All equations used must be stated separately and then clearly substituted if required. Many candidates will look at the end product and somehow end up with the required answer. The marker has to ensure that the path to the solution is clear. It is good practice to state why certain equations are used, explaining the Physics behind them.

### Definitions

Know and understand definitions given in the course. Definitions often come from the interpretation of an equation.

## Diagrams

Use a ruler and the appropriate labels. Angles will be important in certain diagrams. Too many candidates attempt to draw ray diagrams freehand.

## Graphs

Read the question and ensure you know what is being asked. Label your graph correctly and do not forget to label the origin.

## "Explain" and "describe" questions

These tend to be done poorly.

- Ensure all points are covered and read over again in order to check there are no mistakes. Try to be clear and to the point, highlighting the relevant Physics.

- Do not use up and down arrows in a description – this may help you in shorthand, but these must be translated to words.

- Be aware some answers require justification. No attempt at a justification can mean no marks awarded.

## Two or more attempts at an answer

Any attempt that you do not want the marker to consider should be scored out. Otherwise zero marks could be awarded.

Do not be tempted to give extra information that might be incorrect – all the marks may not be awarded if there are incorrect pieces of information. For example, this might include converting **incorrectly** m to nm in the last line of an answer, when it is not required.

**At the end of the exam, if you have time, quickly go over each answer and make sure you have the correct unit inserted.**

## Experimental descriptions/planning

You could well be called on to describe an experimental set-up. Ensure your description is clear enough for another person to repeat it, and include a clearly labelled diagram.

## Suggested improvements to the experimental procedure

Look at the percentage uncertainties in the measured quantities and decide which is most significant. Suggest how the size of this uncertainty could be reduced – do not suggest using better apparatus! It might be better to repeat readings, so that random uncertainty is reduced or increase distances to reduce the percentage uncertainty in scale reading. There could be a systematic uncertainty that is affecting all readings. It really depends on the experiment. Use your judgement.

# Handling data

## Relationships

There are two methods to prove a direct or inverse relationship.

### Graphical approach

Plot the graphs with the appropriate x and y values and look for a straight line – better plotted in pencil in case of mistakes. **Do not force a line through the origin!**

(A vs B for a direct relationship, C vs $\frac{1}{D}$ for an inverse relationship)

> **Using the equation of a straight line, y = mx + c.**
>
> **Be aware that the gradient of the line can often lead to required values.**
>
> Example: Finding the permeability of free space.
>
> $B = \frac{\mu_0 I}{2\pi r}$
>
> Express $B = \frac{\mu_0}{2\pi r} I$ in the form of y = mx + c (c = 0)
>
> By plotting the graph of B against I, the value of the gradient will give $\frac{\mu_0}{2\pi r}$
>
> (Note: the line should not be forced through the origin.)

The value of C can often indicate a systematic uncertainty in the experiment. Ensure you are clear on how to calculate the gradient of a line.

### Algebraic approach

If it appears that A $\propto$ B then calculate the value of $\frac{A}{B}$ **for all values**.

If these show that $\frac{A}{B}$ = k then the relationship holds.

If it appears that C $\propto \frac{1}{D}$ then calculate the value C.D **for all values**.

If these show that C.D = k then the relationship holds.

## Uncertainties

In this area, you must understand the following:

- systematic, calibration, scale reading (analogue and digital) and random uncertainties
- percentage/fractional uncertainties
- combinations – Pythagorean relationship
- absolute uncertainty in the final answer (give to one significant figure).

For your lab work, it is always useful and less time consuming to use a spreadsheet package to shortcut calculations, plot graphs and estimate uncertainties. Just ensure that if plotting a graph, it is at least half a page in size and use the smallest grid lines available.

## Significant figures

**Do not** round off in intermediate calculations, but round off in the final answer to an appropriate number of figures.

**Rounding off to three significant figures in the final answer will generally be acceptable.**

## Prefixes

Ensure you know all the required prefixes and be able to convert them to the correct power of 10.

## Open-ended questions

There will be two open-ended questions in the paper each worth 3 marks. Some candidates look upon these as mini essays.

Remember each is worth only 3 marks and they give the opportunity to demonstrate knowledge and understanding. **However, do not spend too long on these.** It might be better to revisit them at the end of the exam. Some students prefer to use bullet points to highlight the main areas of understanding.

Below is some advice on each unit. Obviously, all points in all units cannot be covered, but hopefully the following can give you a start in what to look out for.

# Unit 1 Rotational Motion and Astrophysics

## Kinematic relationships

**Calculus — equations of motion**

$$s = f(t) - \text{given}$$

Be clear that differentiating once gives the velocity, differentiating twice gives the acceleration.

$$a = f(t) - \text{given}$$

Integrating once gives the velocity, integrating twice gives the displacement. Remember to take into account the constant of integration each time by considering the limits or initial conditions.

**Circular Motion**

Make a two column table with the headings "Linear" and "Circular". On the left-hand side, write down all the equations you have come across in Higher, starting with speed and then the equations of motion. On the right-hand side, add all the equivalent equations for circular motion.

| Linear | Circular |
|---|---|
| $v = \dfrac{s}{t}$ | $\omega = \dfrac{\theta}{t}$ |
| $v = u + at$ | $\omega = \omega_0 + \alpha t$ |
| | |
| | |
| | |

Add to these as you progress through the course.

## Central force

There will often be a question on **central** or **centripetal force**. Remember this is the force that acts on an object causing the object to follow a circular path.

**There is no outward (centrifugal) force acting on that object** and it would be good advice **not to mention this force** in your description.

It is worth noting that a fun fair ride might give the impression of feeling an outward force acting on a person, but this is an unreal force – they just think the force is outward. In fact, it is the inward force from the seat that enables you to follow the circular path.

The same will apply with a "loop the loop" ride where, at the top of the loop, the track and weight of the car supplies the required centripetal force.

**Moment of inertia** can be defined as a measure of the resistance to angular acceleration about a given axis (resistance to change).

## Gravitation

**Circular motion and planetary motion**

The key to calculating the period, T, of motion of a planet or satellite lies with gravitational force supplying the central force, that is:

$$\frac{GMm}{r^2} = mr\omega^2 \text{ then use } \omega = \frac{2\pi}{T} \text{ to find } T.$$

**Escape velocity derivation**

The starting point is the realisation when the object has escaped the pull of gravity **then $E_T = 0$**.

For example, $E_T = E_k + E_p = \dfrac{1}{2}mv^2 - \dfrac{GMm}{r} = 0.$

Rearrange the equation to obtain the **expression for v.**

$\left(\text{Note that } E_p = -\dfrac{GMm}{r}\right)$

**General relativity**

Remember the higher the altitude, then the gravitational field will be less, **which means clocks will run fast**. GPS systems have to take this into account, otherwise the position determined on Earth would be incorrect.

Mass curves spacetime which causes gravitational pull – rubber sheet analogy.

**Stellar Physics**

Become familiar with the Hertzsprung-Russell (H-R) diagram – stellar evolution.

# Unit 2 Quanta and Waves

## Bohr model of the atom

Many candidates omit the fact that the angular momentum of the electrons is quantised.

## Wave particle duality

Experimental evidence is often confused.

- Electron diffraction through crystals – particles as waves.

- Photoelectric effect – waves as particles.

## Uncertainty principle

It is difficult to measure something precisely without the measuring procedure affecting what you are trying to measure!

## Simple harmonic motion: know the definition of SHM

Be able to derive the velocity (differentiate once) and acceleration (differentiate again) given the expression for displacement:

$$y = A\sin\omega t \text{ or } x = A\cos\omega t$$

From v and a the expressions for the maximum velocity and maximum acceleration can be found. (These occur when the maximum value of cos or sin = 1.)

## Waves

**Wave Equation**

$$y = A\sin 2\pi\left(ft - \frac{x}{\lambda}\right)$$

Just knowing the coefficients of t and x in the wave equation allows the retrieval of frequency, wavelength and the speed of the wave,

$$\text{Coefficient of } t = 2\pi f$$

$$\text{Coefficient of } x = \frac{2\pi}{\lambda}$$

**Remember the $2\pi$!**

**Standing or Stationary waves**

Remember these are produced when a reflected wave interferes with the incident wave causing maxima (antinodes) and minima (nodes).

# Unit 3 Electromagnetism

## Electric field strength

**Parallel plates**

(uniform field between plates)

$$E = \frac{V}{d}$$

**Point charge**

$$E = \frac{Q}{4\pi\varepsilon_0 r^2}$$

Candidates often mix up these formulae for electric field strength. They are quite different!

## Ferromagnetism

Certain materials can become magnetised due to the alignment of their magnetic dipoles.

## Charged particles in a magnetic field

A circular orbit will be produced if the charged particle cuts the field at 90°.

The central force is produced by the magnetic force acting on the particle.

$$\frac{mv^2}{r} = Bqv$$

If the charge enters the field at an angle **less than 90°** then the resultant path will be **helical**.

An example of this would be charged particles being deflected by the Earth's magnetic field to the North or South poles producing the borealis.

**Candidates should be able to explain why the resulting motion is helical.**

Treat this as two components of velocity:

$V_H$ = constant and moves in the direction of field lines – no force acting.

$V_V$ = 90° to the field which produces a central force causing the charge particle to follow a circular path.

## Back emf in an inductor (coil)

$$E = -L\frac{dI}{dt}$$

Remember that the back emf is produced by a changing current, which in turn produces a **changing magnetic field** throughout the coil. Many candidates omit this in their explanation.

Be aware that if asked to calculate the inductance L (or the rate of change of current) and a **negative answer** is obtained then **there has been an error. Invariably the fact that the induced emf is negative has not been taken into account.**

For example:

$$E = 9V \frac{dI}{dt}$$
$$= 5\,As^{-1}$$
$$E = -L\frac{dI}{dt}$$
$$9 = -L \times 5$$
$$L = -1\cdot8\,H$$

**This is incorrect!**

$$E = -9V \frac{dI}{dt}$$
$$= 5\,As^{-1}$$
$$E = -L\frac{dI}{dt}$$
$$-9 = -L \times 5$$
$$L = 1\cdot8\,H$$

**This is correct!**

ADVANCED HIGHER

# 2015 Specimen Question Paper

# AH

National
Qualifications
SPECIMEN ONLY

Mark

## SQ29/AH/01

# Physics

Date — Not applicable

Duration — 2 hours 30 minutes

**Fill in these boxes and read what is printed below.**

Full name of centre

Town

Forename(s)

Surname

Number of seat

Date of birth

| Day | Month | Year |
|-----|-------|------|
| D D | M M | Y Y |

Scottish candidate number

**Total marks — 140**

Attempt ALL questions.

Reference may be made to the Physics Relationships Sheet and the Data Sheet on *Page two*.

Write your answers clearly in the spaces provided in this booklet. Additional space for answers is provided at the end of this booklet. If you use this space you must clearly identify the question number you are attempting. Any rough work must be written in this booklet. You should score through your rough work when you have written your final copy.

Use **blue** or **black** ink.

Before leaving the examination room you must give this booklet to the Invigilator; if you do not, you may lose all the marks for this paper.

**DATA SHEET**
COMMON PHYSICAL QUANTITIES

| Quantity | Symbol | Value | Quantity | Symbol | Value |
|---|---|---|---|---|---|
| Gravitational acceleration on Earth | $g$ | $9 \cdot 8 \, \text{m s}^{-2}$ | Mass of electron | $m_e$ | $9 \cdot 11 \times 10^{-31} \, \text{kg}$ |
| Radius of Earth | $R_E$ | $6 \cdot 4 \times 10^6 \, \text{m}$ | Charge on electron | $e$ | $-1 \cdot 60 \times 10^{-19} \, \text{C}$ |
| Mass of Earth | $M_E$ | $6 \cdot 0 \times 10^{24} \, \text{kg}$ | Mass of neutron | $m_n$ | $1 \cdot 675 \times 10^{-27} \, \text{kg}$ |
| Mass of Moon | $M_M$ | $7 \cdot 3 \times 10^{22} \, \text{kg}$ | Mass of proton | $m_p$ | $1 \cdot 673 \times 10^{-27} \, \text{kg}$ |
| Radius of Moon | $R_M$ | $1 \cdot 7 \times 10^6 \, \text{m}$ | Mass of alpha particle | $m_a$ | $6 \cdot 645 \times 10^{-27} \, \text{kg}$ |
| Mean Radius of Moon Orbit | | $3 \cdot 84 \times 10^8 \, \text{m}$ | Charge on alpha particle | | $3 \cdot 20 \times 10^{-19} \, \text{C}$ |
| Solar radius | | $6 \cdot 955 \times 10^8 \, \text{m}$ | Planck's constant | $h$ | $6 \cdot 63 \times 10^{-34} \, \text{J s}$ |
| Mass of Sun | | $2 \cdot 0 \times 10^{30} \, \text{kg}$ | Permittivity of free space | $\varepsilon_0$ | $8 \cdot 85 \times 10^{-12} \, \text{F m}^{-1}$ |
| 1 AU | | $1 \cdot 5 \times 10^{11} \, \text{m}$ | Permeability of free space | $\mu_0$ | $4\pi \times 10^{-7} \, \text{H m}^{-1}$ |
| Stefan-Boltzmann constant | $\sigma$ | $5 \cdot 67 \times 10^{-8} \, \text{W m}^{-2} \text{K}^{-4}$ | Speed of light in vacuum | $c$ | $3 \cdot 0 \times 10^8 \, \text{m s}^{-1}$ |
| Universal constant of gravitation | $G$ | $6 \cdot 67 \times 10^{-11} \, \text{m}^3 \, \text{kg}^{-1} \text{s}^{-2}$ | Speed of sound in air | $v$ | $3 \cdot 4 \times 10^2 \, \text{m s}^{-1}$ |

REFRACTIVE INDICES
The refractive indices refer to sodium light of wavelength 589 nm and to substances at a temperature of 273 K.

| Substance | Refractive index | Substance | Refractive index |
|---|---|---|---|
| Diamond | 2·42 | Glycerol | 1·47 |
| Glass | 1·51 | Water | 1·33 |
| Ice | 1·31 | Air | 1·00 |
| Perspex | 1·49 | Magnesium Fluoride | 1·38 |

SPECTRAL LINES

| Element | Wavelength/nm | Colour | Element | Wavelength/nm | Colour |
|---|---|---|---|---|---|
| Hydrogen | 656 | Red | Cadmium | 644 | Red |
| | 486 | Blue-green | | 509 | Green |
| | 434 | Blue-violet | | 480 | Blue |
| | 410 | Violet | | *Lasers* | |
| | 397 | Ultraviolet | Element | Wavelength/nm | Colour |
| | 389 | Ultraviolet | Carbon dioxide | 9550 } 10590 } | Infrared |
| Sodium | 589 | Yellow | Helium-neon | 633 | Red |

PROPERTIES OF SELECTED MATERIALS

| Substance | Density/ kg m$^{-3}$ | Melting Point/ K | Boiling Point/K | Specific Heat Capacity/ J kg$^{-1}$ K$^{-1}$ | Specific Latent Heat of Fusion/ J kg$^{-1}$ | Specific Latent Heat of Vaporisation/ J kg$^{-1}$ |
|---|---|---|---|---|---|---|
| Aluminium | $2 \cdot 70 \times 10^3$ | 933 | 2623 | $9 \cdot 02 \times 10^2$ | $3 \cdot 95 \times 10^5$ | . . . . |
| Copper | $8 \cdot 96 \times 10^3$ | 1357 | 2853 | $3 \cdot 86 \times 10^2$ | $2 \cdot 05 \times 10^5$ | . . . . |
| Glass | $2 \cdot 60 \times 10^3$ | 1400 | . . . . | $6 \cdot 70 \times 10^2$ | . . . . | . . . . |
| Ice | $9 \cdot 20 \times 10^2$ | 273 | . . . . | $2 \cdot 10 \times 10^3$ | $3 \cdot 34 \times 10^5$ | . . . . |
| Glycerol | $1 \cdot 26 \times 10^3$ | 291 | 563 | $2 \cdot 43 \times 10^3$ | $1 \cdot 81 \times 10^5$ | $8 \cdot 30 \times 10^5$ |
| Methanol | $7 \cdot 91 \times 10^2$ | 175 | 338 | $2 \cdot 52 \times 10^3$ | $9 \cdot 9 \times 10^4$ | $1 \cdot 12 \times 10^6$ |
| Sea Water | $1 \cdot 02 \times 10^3$ | 264 | 377 | $3 \cdot 93 \times 10^3$ | . . . . | . . . . |
| Water | $1 \cdot 00 \times 10^3$ | 273 | 373 | $4 \cdot 19 \times 10^3$ | $3 \cdot 34 \times 10^5$ | $2 \cdot 26 \times 10^6$ |
| Air | 1·29 | . . . . | . . . . | . . . . | . . . . | . . . . |
| Hydrogen | $9 \cdot 0 \times 10^{-2}$ | 14 | 20 | $1 \cdot 43 \times 10^4$ | . . . . | $4 \cdot 50 \times 10^5$ |
| Nitrogen | 1·25 | 63 | 77 | $1 \cdot 04 \times 10^3$ | . . . . | $2 \cdot 00 \times 10^5$ |
| Oxygen | 1·43 | 55 | 90 | $9 \cdot 18 \times 10^2$ | . . . . | $2 \cdot 40 \times 10^4$ |

The gas densities refer to a temperature of 273 K and a pressure of $1 \cdot 01 \times 10^5$ Pa.

**Total marks — 140 marks**

**Attempt ALL questions**

1.  Water is removed from clothes during the spin cycle of a washing machine. The drum holding the clothes has a maximum spin rate of 1250 revolutions per minute.

Figure 1A

(a) Show that the maximum angular velocity of the drum is 131 rad s⁻¹.

2

*Space for working and answer*

(b) At the start of a spin cycle the drum has an angular velocity of 7·50 rad s⁻¹. It then takes 12·0 seconds to accelerate to the maximum angular velocity.

   (i) Calculate the angular acceleration of the drum during the 12·0 seconds, assuming the acceleration is uniform.

3

*Space for working and answer*

MARKS | DO NOT WRITE IN THIS MARGIN

**1. (b) (continued)**

(ii) Determine how many revolutions the drum will make during the 12·0 seconds.

**5**

*Space for working and answer*

(c) When the drum is rotating at maximum angular velocity, an item of wet clothing of mass $1·5 \times 10^{-2}$ kg rotates at a distance of 0·28 m from the axis of rotation as shown in Figure 1B.

0·28 m

item of clothing

Figure 1B

Calculate the centripetal force acting on the item of clothing.

**3**

*Space for working and answer*

MARKS | DO NOT WRITE IN THIS MARGIN

1.  (continued)

(d)  The outer surface of the drum has small holes as shown in Figure 1C. These holes allow most of the water to be removed.

Figure 1C

(i)  Explain why the water separates from the item of clothing during the spin cycle.

**2**

(ii)  The drum rotates in an anticlockwise direction. Indicate on Figure 1D the direction taken by a water droplet as it leaves the drum.

**1**

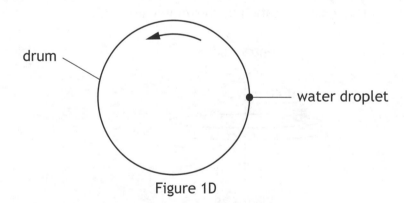

drum

water droplet

Figure 1D

(iii)  Explain what happens to the value of the force on an item of clothing inside the drum as it rotates at its maximum angular velocity.

**2**

MARKS | DO NOT WRITE IN THIS MARGIN

2. A disc of mass 6·0 kg and radius 0·50 m is allowed to rotate freely about its central axis as shown in Figure 2A.

central axis

Figure 2A

(a) Show that the moment of inertia of the disc is 0·75 kg m². **2**

*Space for working and answer*

(b) The disc is rotating with an angular velocity of 12 rad s⁻¹. A cube of mass 2·0 kg is then dropped onto the disc. The cube remains at a distance of 0·40 m from the axis of rotation as shown in Figure 2B.

central axis

0·40 m

Figure 2B

MARKS | DO NOT WRITE IN THIS MARGIN

**2.** **(b) (continued)**

(i) Determine the total moment of inertia of the disc and cube.    **3**

*Space for working and answer*

(ii) Calculate the angular velocity of the disc after the cube lands.    **3**

*Space for working and answer*

(iii) State **one** assumption you have made in your response to b(ii).    **1**

(c) The cube is removed and the disc is again made to rotate with a constant angular velocity of 12 rad s⁻¹. A sphere of mass 2·0 kg is then dropped onto the disc at a distance of 0·40 m from the axis as shown in Figure 2C.

0·40 m

Figure 2C

State whether the resulting angular velocity of the disc is greater than, the same as, or less than, the value calculated in b(ii).

You must justify your answer.    **2**

MARKS | DO NOT WRITE IN THIS MARGIN

3. The International Space Station (ISS) is in orbit around the Earth.

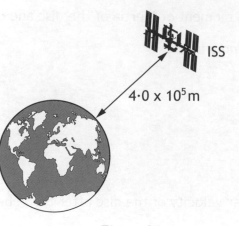

ISS

4·0 x 10⁵ m

Figure 3A

(a) (i) The gravitational pull of the Earth keeps the ISS in orbit.

Show that for an orbit of radius $r$ the period $T$ is given by the expression

$$T = 2\pi\sqrt{\frac{r^3}{GM_E}}$$

where the symbols have their usual meaning.

**2**

(ii) Calculate the period of orbit of the ISS when it is at an altitude of $4{\cdot}0 \times 10^5$ m above the surface of the Earth.

**2**

*Space for working and answer*

3.   (continued)

(b)   The graph in Figure 3B shows how the altitude of the ISS has varied over time.   Reductions in altitude are due to the drag of the Earth's atmosphere acting on the ISS.

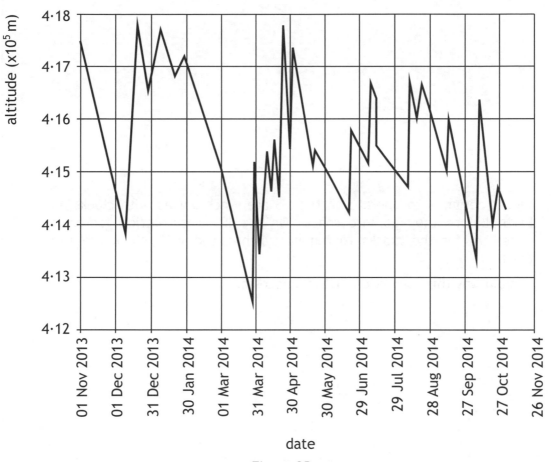

date

Figure 3B

(i)   Determine the value of Earth's gravitational field strength at the ISS on 1 March 2014.

*Space for working and answer*

4

MARKS | DO NOT WRITE IN THIS MARGIN

3.   (b)  (continued)

(ii)  In 2011 the average altitude of the ISS was increased from 350 km to 400 km.

Give an advantage of operating the ISS at this higher altitude.    **1**

(c)  Clocks designed to operate on the ISS are synchronised with clocks on Earth before they go into space. On the ISS a correction factor is necessary for the clocks to remain synchronised with clocks on the Earth.

Explain why this correction factor is necessary.    **2**

MARKS | DO NOT WRITE IN THIS MARGIN

4. The constellation Orion, shown in Figure 4A, is a common sight in the winter sky above Scotland.

Figure 4A

Two of the stars in this constellation are known as Betelgeuse and Rigel. Their positions are shown on the Hertzsprung—Russell (H—R) diagram in Figure 4B.

MARKS | DO NOT WRITE IN THIS MARGIN

**4.    (continued)**

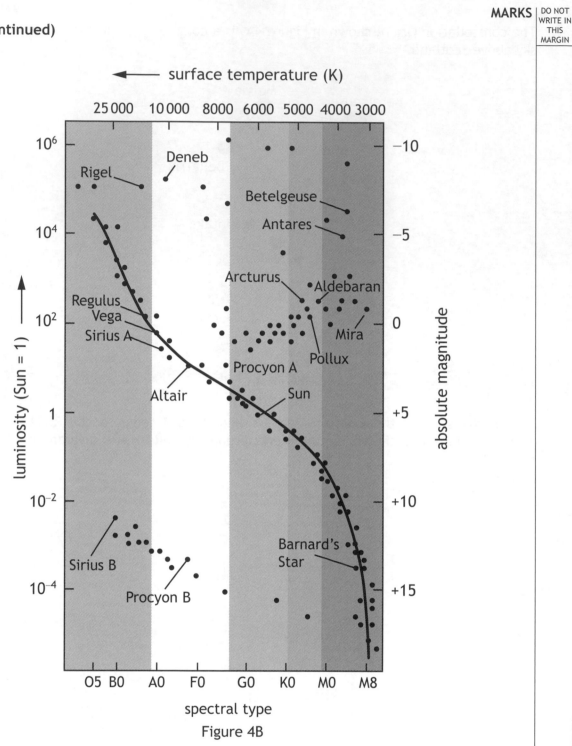

Figure 4B

(a)   Using the H—R diagram, predict the colour of Betelgeuse.          1

MARKS | DO NOT WRITE IN THIS MARGIN

4. **(continued)**

(b) The table shows some of the physical properties of Rigel.

| Property of Rigel | |
|---|---|
| Surface temperature | $(1\cdot20 \pm 0\cdot05) \times 10^4\,\text{K}$ |
| Radius | $(5\cdot49 \pm 0\cdot50) \times 10^{10}\,\text{m}$ |
| Mass | $18 \pm 1$ solar masses |
| Distance to Earth | $773 \pm 150$ light years |

(i) (A) Calculate the luminosity of Rigel.    3

*Space for working and answer*

(B) State the assumption made in your calculation.    1

(ii) Calculate the absolute uncertainty in the value of the luminosity of Rigel.    4

*Space for working and answer*

MARKS | DO NOT WRITE IN THIS MARGIN

4. **(continued)**

(c) Calculate the apparent brightness of Rigel as observed from the Earth. **4**

*Space for working and answer*

(d) Betelgeuse is not on the Main Sequence region of the H—R diagram. Describe the changes that have taken place in Betelgeuse since leaving the Main Sequence. **2**

MARKS | DO NOT WRITE IN THIS MARGIN

5.  Figure 5A shows a snowboarder in a half pipe. The snowboarder is moving between positions P and Q. The total mass of the snowboarder and board is 85 kg.

Figure 5A

A student attempts to model the motion of the snowboarder as simple harmonic motion (SHM).

The student uses measurements of amplitude and period to produce the displacement-time graph shown in Figure 5B.

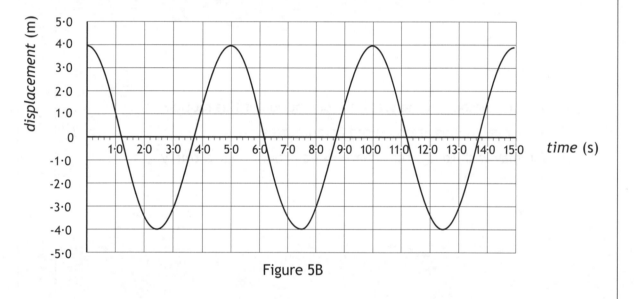

Figure 5B

(a)   (i)   State what is meant by the term *simple harmonic motion*.    1

MARKS

**5.** **(a)** **(continued)**

   (ii) Determine the angular frequency of the motion.          4

   *Space for working and answer*

   (iii) Calculate the maximum acceleration experienced by the snowboarder on the halfpipe.          3

   *Space for working and answer*

   (iv) Sketch a velocity-time graph for one period of this motion. Numerical values are required on both axes.          3

   You may wish to use the square-ruled paper on *Page thirty*.

   (v) Calculate the maximum potential energy of the snowboarder.          3

   *Space for working and answer*

MARKS | DO NOT WRITE IN THIS MARGIN

**5. (continued)**

(b) Detailed video analysis shows that the snowboarder's motion is not fully described by the SHM model.

Using your knowledge of physics, comment on possible reasons for this discrepancy.

3

**6.** The Bohr model of the hydrogen atom consists of a single electron orbiting a single proton. Due to the quantisation of angular momentum, in this model, the electron can only orbit at particular radii.

Figure 6A shows an electron with principal quantum number $n=1$.

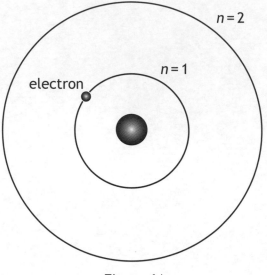

Figure 6A

(a) Explain what gives rise to the centripetal force acting on the electron.    **1**

MARKS | DO NOT WRITE IN THIS MARGIN

6.  (continued)

(b)    (i)  Show that the kinetic energy of the electron is given by

$$E_k = \frac{e^2}{8\pi\varepsilon_0 r}$$

where the symbols have their usual meaning.                    2

(ii)  Calculate the kinetic energy for an electron with orbital radius 0·21 nm.                                                           2

*Space for working and answer*

(c)  Calculate the principal quantum number for an electron with angular momentum $4\cdot22 \times 10^{-34}\,\text{kg m}^2\text{s}^{-1}$.                    3

*Space for working and answer*

MARKS | DO NOT WRITE IN THIS MARGIN

**6.    (continued)**

(d)  Heisenberg's uncertainty principle addresses some of the limitations of classical physics in describing quantum phenomena.

(i)  The uncertainty in an experimental measurement of the momentum of an electron in a hydrogen atom was determined to be $\pm 1{\cdot}5 \times 10^{-26}\,\text{kg}\,\text{m}\,\text{s}^{-1}$.

Calculate the minimum uncertainty in the position of the electron.    **3**

*Space for working and answer*

(ii)  In a scanning tunnelling microscope (STM) a sharp metallic tip is brought very close to the surface of a conductor. As the tip is moved back and forth, an electric current can be detected due to the movement ("tunnelling") of electrons across the air gap between the tip and the conductor, as shown in Figure 6B.

STM tip

tunnelling electrons

Figure 6B

According to classical physics, electrons should not be able to cross the gap as the kinetic energy of each electron is insufficient to overcome the repulsion between electrons in the STM tip and the surface.

Explain why an electron is able to cross the gap.    **3**

MARKS | DO NOT WRITE IN THIS MARGIN

7. When a microwave oven is switched on a stationary wave is formed inside the oven.

   (a) Explain how a stationary wave is formed.   1

   (b) A student carries out an experiment to determine the speed of light using a microwave oven. The turntable is removed from the oven and bread covered in butter is placed inside. The oven is switched on for a short time, after which the student observes that the butter has melted only in certain spots, as shown in Figure 7A.

   melted spot
   Figure 7A

   Explain why the butter has melted in certain spots and not in others.   2

MARKS

7.  **(continued)**

(c)  The student measures the distance between the first hot spot and fifth hot spot as 264 mm.

264 mm

Figure 7B

From the data obtained by the student determine the wavelength of the microwaves.

*Space for working and answer*

2

(d)  The quoted value for the frequency of the microwaves is 2·45 GHz. The student calculates the speed of light using data from the experiment.

Show that the value obtained by the student for the speed of light is $3·23 \times 10^8 \, \text{m s}^{-1}$.

*Space for working and answer*

2

(e)  The student repeats the experiment and obtains the following values for the speed of light,

$3·26 \times 10^8 \, \text{m s}^{-1}$, $3·19 \times 10^8 \, \text{m s}^{-1}$, $3·23 \times 10^8 \, \text{m s}^{-1}$, $3·21 \times 10^8 \, \text{m s}^{-1}$.

Comment on both the accuracy and precision of the student's results.

2

**8.** A beam of electrons is incident on a grating as shown in Figure 8A.

zinc sulfide coated screen

grating

electron gun

Figure 8A

(a) After passing through the grating the electrons are incident on a zinc sulfide coated screen. The coating emits light when struck by electrons.

Describe the pattern observed on the screen.

1

(b) Scientists perform similar experiments with large molecules. One such molecule is buckminsterfullerene (C60) with a mass of $1 \cdot 20 \times 10^{-24}$ kg.

For C60 molecules with a velocity of $220\,\text{m s}^{-1}$ estimate the slit spacing required to produce a pattern comparable to that observed for the electrons. You must justify your answer by calculation.

4

*Space for working and answer*

MARKS | DO NOT WRITE IN THIS MARGIN

9. As part of a physics project a student carried out experiments to obtain values for the permeability of free space and the permittivity of free space.

The results obtained by the student were

permeability of free space, $\mu_0 = (1\cdot32\pm0\cdot05)\times10^{-6}\,\mathrm{H\,m^{-1}}$

permittivity of free space, $\varepsilon_0 = (8\cdot93\pm0\cdot07)\times10^{-12}\,\mathrm{F\,m^{-1}}$

(a) State the number of significant figures in the value of each result.

**1**

(b) Use these results to determine a value for the speed of light.

Your answer must be consistent with (a).

**3**

*Space for working and answer*

(c) (i) Determine which of the uncertainties obtained by the student is more significant for the calculation of the speed of light.

You must justify your answer by calculation.

**3**

*Space for working and answer*

(ii) Calculate the absolute uncertainty in the value obtained for the speed of light.

**2**

*Space for working and answer*

MARKS | DO NOT WRITE IN THIS MARGIN

10. (a) Two point charges $Q_1$ and $Q_2$ are separated by a distance of 0·60 m as shown in Figure 10A. The charge on $Q_1$ is −8·0 nC. The electric field strength at point X is zero.

−8·0 nC      X

$Q_1$             $Q_2$

0·40 m     0·20 m

Figure 10A

(i) State what is meant by *electric field strength*.     1

(ii) Show that the charge on $Q_2$ is −2·0 nC.     2

*Space for working and answer*

(iii) Calculate the electrical potential at point X.     5

*Space for working and answer*

MARKS | DO NOT WRITE IN THIS MARGIN

**10.    (continued)**

(b)

Figure 10B

(i)   Calculate the electrical potential at point P.    **3**

*Space for working and answer*

(ii)   Determine the energy required to move a charge of +1·0 nC from point X to point P.    **4**

*Space for working and answer*

MARKS | DO NOT WRITE IN THIS MARGIN

11. The Nobel prize winning physicist Richard Feynman once stated "things on a small scale behave nothing like things on a large scale".

Using your knowledge of physics, comment on his statement.    3

MARKS | DO NOT WRITE IN THIS MARGIN

12. A student carries out a series of experiments to investigate properties of capacitors in a.c. circuits.

(a) The student connects a 5·0 µF capacitor to an a.c. supply of e.m.f. 15 V$_{rms}$ and negligible internal resistance as shown in Figure 12A.

15 V$_{rms}$

5·0 µF

Figure 12A

The frequency of the a.c. supply is 65 Hz.

(i) Calculate the reactance of the capacitor.    **3**

*Space for working and answer*

(ii) Determine the value of the current in the circuit.    **3**

*Space for working and answer*

MARKS | DO NOT WRITE IN THIS MARGIN

12. **(continued)**

(b) The student uses the following circuit to determine the capacitance of a second capacitor.

signal generator

**Figure 12B**

The student obtains the following data.

| Reactance (Ω) | Frequency (Hz) |
|---|---|
| $1.60 \times 10^6$ | 10 |
| $6.47 \times 10^5$ | 40 |
| $2.99 \times 10^5$ | 100 |
| $1.52 \times 10^5$ | 200 |
| $6.35 \times 10^4$ | 500 |
| $3.18 \times 10^4$ | 1000 |

(i) On the square-ruled paper on *Page thirty*, plot a graph that would be suitable to determine the capacitance.  **4**

(ii) Use your graph to determine the capacitance of this capacitor.  **3**

*Space for working and answer*

**[END OF SPECIMEN QUESTION PAPER]**

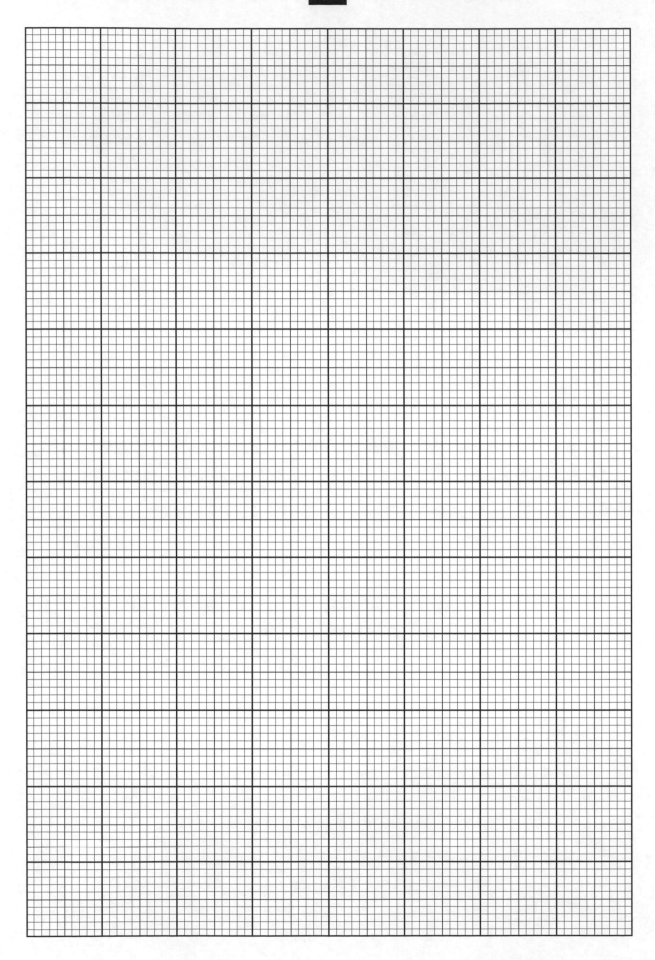

**MARKS** | DO NOT WRITE IN THIS MARGIN

**ADDITIONAL SPACE FOR ANSWERS AND ROUGH WORK**

**ADDITIONAL SPACE FOR ANSWERS AND ROUGH WORK**

**ADVANCED HIGHER**

# 2016

National
Qualifications
2016

X757/77/11

**Physics
Relationships Sheet**

TUESDAY, 24 MAY
9:00 AM — 11:30 AM

# Relationships required for Physics Advanced Higher

$$v = \frac{ds}{dt}$$

$$a = \frac{dv}{dt} = \frac{d^2s}{dt^2}$$

$$v = u + at$$

$$s = ut + \frac{1}{2}at^2$$

$$v^2 = u^2 + 2as$$

$$\omega = \frac{d\theta}{dt}$$

$$\alpha = \frac{d\omega}{dt} = \frac{d^2\theta}{dt^2}$$

$$\omega = \omega_o + \alpha t$$

$$\theta = \omega_o t + \frac{1}{2}\alpha t^2$$

$$\omega^2 = \omega_o^2 + 2\alpha\theta$$

$$s = r\theta$$

$$v = r\omega$$

$$a_t = r\alpha$$

$$a_r = \frac{v^2}{r} = r\omega^2$$

$$F = \frac{mv^2}{r} = mr\omega^2$$

$$T = Fr$$

$$T = I\alpha$$

$$L = mvr = mr^2\omega$$

$$L = I\omega$$

$$E_K = \frac{1}{2}I\omega^2$$

$$F = G\frac{Mm}{r^2}$$

$$V = -\frac{GM}{r}$$

$$v = \sqrt{\frac{2GM}{r}}$$

apparent brightness, $b = \dfrac{L}{4\pi r^2}$

Power per unit area $= \sigma T^4$

$$L = 4\pi r^2 \sigma T^4$$

$$r_{Schwarzschild} = \frac{2GM}{c^2}$$

$$E = hf$$

$$\lambda = \frac{h}{p}$$

$$mvr = \frac{nh}{2\pi}$$

$$\Delta x\, \Delta p_x \geq \frac{h}{4\pi}$$

$$\Delta E\, \Delta t \geq \frac{h}{4\pi}$$

$$F = qvB$$

$$\omega = 2\pi f$$

$$a = \frac{d^2y}{dt^2} = -\omega^2 y$$

$y = A\cos\omega t$ or $y = A\sin\omega t$

$v = \pm\omega\sqrt{(A^2 - y^2)}$

$E_K = \frac{1}{2}m\omega^2(A^2 - y^2)$

$E_P = \frac{1}{2}m\omega^2 y^2$

$y = A\sin 2\pi(ft - \frac{x}{\lambda})$

$E = kA^2$

$\phi = \frac{2\pi x}{\lambda}$

optical path difference $= m\lambda$ or $\left(m+\frac{1}{2}\right)\lambda$

where $m = 0, 1, 2....$

$\Delta x = \frac{\lambda l}{2d}$

$d = \frac{\lambda}{4n}$

$\Delta x = \frac{\lambda D}{d}$

$n = \tan i_P$

$F = \frac{Q_1 Q_2}{4\pi\varepsilon_o r^2}$

$E = \frac{Q}{4\pi\varepsilon_o r^2}$

$V = \frac{Q}{4\pi\varepsilon_o r}$

$F = QE$

$V = Ed$

$F = IlB\sin\theta$

$B = \frac{\mu_o I}{2\pi r}$

$c = \frac{1}{\sqrt{\varepsilon_o \mu_o}}$

$t = RC$

$X_C = \frac{V}{I}$

$X_C = \frac{1}{2\pi f C}$

$\varepsilon = -L\frac{dI}{dt}$

$E = \frac{1}{2}LI^2$

$X_L = \frac{V}{I}$

$X_L = 2\pi f L$

$\frac{\Delta W}{W} = \sqrt{\left(\frac{\Delta X}{X}\right)^2 + \left(\frac{\Delta Y}{Y}\right)^2 + \left(\frac{\Delta Z}{Z}\right)^2}$

$\Delta W = \sqrt{\Delta X^2 + \Delta Y^2 + \Delta Z^2}$

$d = \bar{v}t$

$s = \bar{v}t$

$v = u + at$

$s = ut + \dfrac{1}{2}at^2$

$v^2 = u^2 + 2as$

$s = \dfrac{1}{2}(u + v)t$

$W = mg$

$F = ma$

$E_W = Fd$

$E_P = mgh$

$E_K = \dfrac{1}{2}mv^2$

$P = \dfrac{E}{t}$

$p = mv$

$Ft = mv - mu$

$F = G\dfrac{Mm}{r^2}$

$t' = \dfrac{t}{\sqrt{1 - \left(\frac{v}{c}\right)^2}}$

$l' = l\sqrt{1 - \left(\frac{v}{c}\right)^2}$

$f_o = f_s\left(\dfrac{v}{v \pm v_s}\right)$

$z = \dfrac{\lambda_{observed} - \lambda_{rest}}{\lambda_{rest}}$

$z = \dfrac{v}{c}$

$v = H_0 d$

$W = QV$

$E = mc^2$

$E = hf$

$E_K = hf - hf_0$

$E_2 - E_1 = hf$

$T = \dfrac{1}{f}$

$v = f\lambda$

$d \sin\theta = m\lambda$

$n = \dfrac{\sin\theta_1}{\sin\theta_2}$

$\dfrac{\sin\theta_1}{\sin\theta_2} = \dfrac{\lambda_1}{\lambda_2} = \dfrac{v_1}{v_2}$

$\sin\theta_c = \dfrac{1}{n}$

$I = \dfrac{k}{d^2}$

$I = \dfrac{P}{A}$

path difference $= m\lambda$ or $\left(m + \dfrac{1}{2}\right)\lambda$ where $m = 0, 1, 2 \ldots$

random uncertainty $= \dfrac{\text{max. value} - \text{min. value}}{\text{number of values}}$

$V_{peak} = \sqrt{2}V_{rms}$

$I_{peak} = \sqrt{2}I_{rms}$

$Q = It$

$V = IR$

$P = IV = I^2R = \dfrac{V^2}{R}$

$R_T = R_1 + R_2 + \ldots$

$\dfrac{1}{R_T} = \dfrac{1}{R_1} + \dfrac{1}{R_2} + \ldots$

$E = V + Ir$

$V_1 = \left(\dfrac{R_1}{R_1 + R_2}\right)V_s$

$\dfrac{V_1}{V_2} = \dfrac{R_1}{R_2}$

$C = \dfrac{Q}{V}$

$E = \dfrac{1}{2}QV = \dfrac{1}{2}CV^2 = \dfrac{1}{2}\dfrac{Q^2}{C}$

# Additional Relationships

## Circle

circumference $= 2\pi r$

area $= \pi r^2$

## Sphere

area $= 4\pi r^2$

volume $= \frac{4}{3}\pi r^3$

## Trigonometry

$$\sin\theta = \frac{\text{opposite}}{\text{hypotenuse}}$$

$$\cos\theta = \frac{\text{adjacent}}{\text{hypotenuse}}$$

$$\tan\theta = \frac{\text{opposite}}{\text{adjacent}}$$

$$\sin^2\theta + \cos^2\theta = 1$$

## Moment of inertia

point mass
$$I = mr^2$$

rod about centre
$$I = \tfrac{1}{12}ml^2$$

rod about end
$$I = \tfrac{1}{3}ml^2$$

disc about centre
$$I = \tfrac{1}{2}mr^2$$

sphere about centre
$$I = \tfrac{2}{5}mr^2$$

## Table of standard derivatives

| $f(x)$ | $f'(x)$ |
|---|---|
| $\sin ax$ | $a\cos ax$ |
| $\cos ax$ | $-a\sin ax$ |

## Table of standard integrals

| $f(x)$ | $\int f(x)dx$ |
|---|---|
| $\sin ax$ | $-\dfrac{1}{a}\cos ax + C$ |
| $\cos ax$ | $\dfrac{1}{a}\sin ax + C$ |

# Electron Arrangements of Elements

**Key**

Atomic number
Symbol
Electron arrangement
Name

## Transition Elements

| Group 1 (1) | Group 2 (2) | (3) | (4) | (5) | (6) | (7) | (8) | (9) | (10) | (11) | (12) | Group 3 (13) | Group 4 (14) | Group 5 (15) | Group 6 (16) | Group 7 (17) | Group 0 (18) |
|---|---|---|---|---|---|---|---|---|---|---|---|---|---|---|---|---|---|
| 1 **H** 1 Hydrogen | | | | | | | | | | | | | | | | | 2 **He** 2 Helium |
| 3 **Li** 2,1 Lithium | 4 **Be** 2,2 Beryllium | | | | | | | | | | | 5 **B** 2,3 Boron | 6 **C** 2,4 Carbon | 7 **N** 2,5 Nitrogen | 8 **O** 2,6 Oxygen | 9 **F** 2,7 Fluorine | 10 **Ne** 2,8 Neon |
| 11 **Na** 2,8,1 Sodium | 12 **Mg** 2,8,2 Magnesium | | | | | | | | | | | 13 **Al** 2,8,3 Aluminium | 14 **Si** 2,8,4 Silicon | 15 **P** 2,8,5 Phosphorus | 16 **S** 2,8,6 Sulphur | 17 **Cl** 2,8,7 Chlorine | 18 **Ar** 2,8,8 Argon |
| 19 **K** 2,8,8,1 Potassium | 20 **Ca** 2,8,8,2 Calcium | 21 **Sc** 2,8,9,2 Scandium | 22 **Ti** 2,8,10,2 Titanium | 23 **V** 2,8,11,2 Vanadium | 24 **Cr** 2,8,13,1 Chromium | 25 **Mn** 2,8,13,2 Manganese | 26 **Fe** 2,8,14,2 Iron | 27 **Co** 2,8,15,2 Cobalt | 28 **Ni** 2,8,16,2 Nickel | 29 **Cu** 2,8,18,1 Copper | 30 **Zn** 2,8,18,2 Zinc | 31 **Ga** 2,8,18,3 Gallium | 32 **Ge** 2,8,18,4 Germanium | 33 **As** 2,8,18,5 Arsenic | 34 **Se** 2,8,18,6 Selenium | 35 **Br** 2,8,18,7 Bromine | 36 **Kr** 2,8,18,8 Krypton |
| 37 **Rb** 2,8,18,8,1 Rubidium | 38 **Sr** 2,8,18,8,2 Strontium | 39 **Y** 2,8,18,9,2 Yttrium | 40 **Zr** 2,8,18,10,2 Zirconium | 41 **Nb** 2,8,18,12,1 Niobium | 42 **Mo** 2,8,18,13,1 Molybdenum | 43 **Tc** 2,8,18,13,2 Technetium | 44 **Ru** 2,8,18,15,1 Ruthenium | 45 **Rh** 2,8,18,16,1 Rhodium | 46 **Pd** 2,8,18,18,0 Palladium | 47 **Ag** 2,8,18,18,1 Silver | 48 **Cd** 2,8,18,18,2 Cadmium | 49 **In** 2,8,18,18,3 Indium | 50 **Sn** 2,8,18,18,4 Tin | 51 **Sb** 2,8,18,18,5 Antimony | 52 **Te** 2,8,18,18,6 Tellurium | 53 **I** 2,8,18,18,7 Iodine | 54 **Xe** 2,8,18,18,8 Xenon |
| 55 **Cs** 2,8,18,18,8,1 Caesium | 56 **Ba** 2,8,18,18,8,2 Barium | 57 **La** 2,8,18,18,9,2 Lanthanum | 72 **Hf** 2,8,18,32,10,2 Hafnium | 73 **Ta** 2,8,18,32,11,2 Tantalum | 74 **W** 2,8,18,32,12,2 Tungsten | 75 **Re** 2,8,18,32,13,2 Rhenium | 76 **Os** 2,8,18,32,14,2 Osmium | 77 **Ir** 2,8,18,32,15,2 Iridium | 78 **Pt** 2,8,18,32,17,1 Platinum | 79 **Au** 2,8,18,32,18,1 Gold | 80 **Hg** 2,8,18,32,18,2 Mercury | 81 **Tl** 2,8,18,32,18,3 Thallium | 82 **Pb** 2,8,18,32,18,4 Lead | 83 **Bi** 2,8,18,32,18,5 Bismuth | 84 **Po** 2,8,18,32,18,6 Polonium | 85 **At** 2,8,18,32,18,7 Astatine | 86 **Rn** 2,8,18,32,18,8 Radon |
| 87 **Fr** 2,8,18,32,18,8,1 Francium | 88 **Ra** 2,8,18,32,18,8,2 Radium | 89 **Ac** 2,8,18,32,18,9,2 Actinium | 104 **Rf** 2,8,18,32,32,10,2 Rutherfordium | 105 **Db** 2,8,18,32,32,11,2 Dubnium | 106 **Sg** 2,8,18,32,32,12,2 Seaborgium | 107 **Bh** 2,8,18,32,32,13,2 Bohrium | 108 **Hs** 2,8,18,32,32,14,2 Hassium | 109 **Mt** 2,8,18,32,32,15,2 Meitnerium | | | | | | | | | |

## Lanthanides

| | | | | | | | | | | | | | |
|---|---|---|---|---|---|---|---|---|---|---|---|---|---|
| 57 **La** 2,8,18,18,9,2 Lanthanum | 58 **Ce** 2,8,18,20,8,2 Cerium | 59 **Pr** 2,8,18,21,8,2 Praseodymium | 60 **Nd** 2,8,18,22,8,2 Neodymium | 61 **Pm** 2,8,18,23,8,2 Promethium | 62 **Sm** 2,8,18,24,8,2 Samarium | 63 **Eu** 2,8,18,25,8,2 Europium | 64 **Gd** 2,8,18,25,9,2 Gadolinium | 65 **Tb** 2,8,18,27,8,2 Terbium | 66 **Dy** 2,8,18,28,8,2 Dysprosium | 67 **Ho** 2,8,18,29,8,2 Holmium | 68 **Er** 2,8,18,30,8,2 Erbium | 69 **Tm** 2,8,18,31,8,2 Thulium | 70 **Yb** 2,8,18,32,8,2 Ytterbium |
| 71 **Lu** 2,8,18,32,9,2 Lutetium | | | | | | | | | | | | | |

## Actinides

| | | | | | | | | | | | | | |
|---|---|---|---|---|---|---|---|---|---|---|---|---|---|
| 89 **Ac** 2,8,18,32,18,9,2 Actinium | 90 **Th** 2,8,18,32,18,10,2 Thorium | 91 **Pa** 2,8,18,32,20,9,2 Protactinium | 92 **U** 2,8,18,32,21,9,2 Uranium | 93 **Np** 2,8,18,32,22,9,2 Neptunium | 94 **Pu** 2,8,18,32,24,8,2 Plutonium | 95 **Am** 2,8,18,32,25,8,2 Americium | 96 **Cm** 2,8,18,32,25,9,2 Curium | 97 **Bk** 2,8,18,32,27,8,2 Berkelium | 98 **Cf** 2,8,18,32,28,8,2 Californium | 99 **Es** 2,8,18,32,29,8,2 Einsteinium | 100 **Fm** 2,8,18,32,30,8,2 Fermium | 101 **Md** 2,8,18,32,31,8,2 Mendelevium | 102 **No** 2,8,18,32,32,8,2 Nobelium |
| 103 **Lr** 2,8,18,32,32,9,2 Lawrencium | | | | | | | | | | | | | |

# AH

**National Qualifications 2016**

Mark

**X757/77/01**

**Physics**

TUESDAY, 24 MAY

9:00 AM — 11:30 AM

---

**Fill in these boxes and read what is printed below.**

Full name of centre

Town

Forename(s)

Surname

Number of seat

Date of birth

Day | Month | Year | Scottish candidate number

**Total marks — 140**

Attempt ALL questions.

Reference may be made to the Physics Relationships Sheet X757/77/11 and the Data Sheet on *Page two*.

Write your answers clearly in the spaces provided in this booklet. Additional space for answers and rough work is provided at the end of this booklet. If you use this space you must clearly identify the question number you are attempting. Any rough work must be written in this booklet. You should score through your rough work when you have written your final copy.

Care should be taken to give an appropriate number of significant figures in the final answers to calculations.

Use **blue** or **black** ink.

Before leaving the examination room you must give this booklet to the Invigilator; if you do not, you may lose all the marks for this paper.

SQA

**DATA SHEET**
**COMMON PHYSICAL QUANTITIES**

| Quantity | Symbol | Value | Quantity | Symbol | Value |
|---|---|---|---|---|---|
| Gravitational acceleration on Earth | $g$ | $9.8\,\text{m s}^{-2}$ | Mass of electron | $m_e$ | $9.11 \times 10^{-31}\,\text{kg}$ |
| Radius of Earth | $R_E$ | $6.4 \times 10^6\,\text{m}$ | Charge on electron | $e$ | $-1.60 \times 10^{-19}\,\text{C}$ |
| Mass of Earth | $M_E$ | $6.0 \times 10^{24}\,\text{kg}$ | Mass of neutron | $m_n$ | $1.675 \times 10^{-27}\,\text{kg}$ |
| Mass of Moon | $M_M$ | $7.3 \times 10^{22}\,\text{kg}$ | Mass of proton | $m_p$ | $1.673 \times 10^{-27}\,\text{kg}$ |
| Radius of Moon | $R_M$ | $1.7 \times 10^6\,\text{m}$ | Mass of alpha particle | $m_a$ | $6.645 \times 10^{-27}\,\text{kg}$ |
| Mean Radius of Moon Orbit | | $3.84 \times 10^8\,\text{m}$ | Charge on alpha particle | | $3.20 \times 10^{-19}\,\text{C}$ |
| Solar radius | | $6.955 \times 10^8\,\text{m}$ | Planck's constant | $h$ | $6.63 \times 10^{-34}\,\text{J s}$ |
| Mass of Sun | | $2.0 \times 10^{30}\,\text{kg}$ | Permittivity of free space | $\varepsilon_0$ | $8.85 \times 10^{-12}\,\text{F m}^{-1}$ |
| 1 AU | | $1.5 \times 10^{11}\,\text{m}$ | Permeability of free space | $\mu_0$ | $4\pi \times 10^{-7}\,\text{H m}^{-1}$ |
| Stefan-Boltzmann constant | $\sigma$ | $5.67 \times 10^{-8}\,\text{W m}^{-2}\text{K}^{-4}$ | Speed of light in vacuum | $c$ | $3.0 \times 10^8\,\text{m s}^{-1}$ |
| Universal constant of gravitation | $G$ | $6.67 \times 10^{-11}\,\text{m}^3\,\text{kg}^{-1}\,\text{s}^{-2}$ | Speed of sound in air | $v$ | $3.4 \times 10^2\,\text{m s}^{-1}$ |

**REFRACTIVE INDICES**
The refractive indices refer to sodium light of wavelength 589 nm and to substances at a temperature of 273 K.

| Substance | Refractive index | Substance | Refractive index |
|---|---|---|---|
| Diamond | 2·42 | Glycerol | 1·47 |
| Glass | 1·51 | Water | 1·33 |
| Ice | 1·31 | Air | 1·00 |
| Perspex | 1·49 | Magnesium Fluoride | 1·38 |

**SPECTRAL LINES**

| Element | Wavelength/nm | Colour | Element | Wavelength/nm | Colour |
|---|---|---|---|---|---|
| Hydrogen | 656 | Red | Cadmium | 644 | Red |
| | 486 | Blue-green | | 509 | Green |
| | 434 | Blue-violet | | 480 | Blue |
| | 410 | Violet | | | |
| | 397 | Ultraviolet | | | |
| | 389 | Ultraviolet | | | |
| Sodium | 589 | Yellow | | | |

| Lasers | | |
|---|---|---|
| Element | Wavelength/nm | Colour |
| Carbon dioxide | 9550 } 10590 | Infrared |
| Helium-neon | 633 | Red |

**PROPERTIES OF SELECTED MATERIALS**

| Substance | Density/ $\text{kg m}^{-3}$ | Melting Point/ K | Boiling Point/K | Specific Heat Capacity/ $\text{J kg}^{-1}\text{K}^{-1}$ | Specific Latent Heat of Fusion/ $\text{J kg}^{-1}$ | Specific Latent Heat of Vaporisation/ $\text{J kg}^{-1}$ |
|---|---|---|---|---|---|---|
| Aluminium | $2.70 \times 10^3$ | 933 | 2623 | $9.02 \times 10^2$ | $3.95 \times 10^5$ | .... |
| Copper | $8.96 \times 10^3$ | 1357 | 2853 | $3.86 \times 10^2$ | $2.05 \times 10^5$ | .... |
| Glass | $2.60 \times 10^3$ | 1400 | .... | $6.70 \times 10^2$ | .... | .... |
| Ice | $9.20 \times 10^2$ | 273 | .... | $2.10 \times 10^3$ | $3.34 \times 10^5$ | .... |
| Glycerol | $1.26 \times 10^3$ | 291 | 563 | $2.43 \times 10^3$ | $1.81 \times 10^5$ | $8.30 \times 10^5$ |
| Methanol | $7.91 \times 10^2$ | 175 | 338 | $2.52 \times 10^3$ | $9.9 \times 10^4$ | $1.12 \times 10^6$ |
| Sea Water | $1.02 \times 10^3$ | 264 | 377 | $3.93 \times 10^3$ | .... | .... |
| Water | $1.00 \times 10^3$ | 273 | 373 | $4.19 \times 10^3$ | $3.34 \times 10^5$ | $2.26 \times 10^6$ |
| Air | 1·29 | .... | .... | .... | .... | .... |
| Hydrogen | $9.0 \times 10^{-2}$ | 14 | 20 | $1.43 \times 10^4$ | .... | $4.50 \times 10^5$ |
| Nitrogen | 1·25 | 63 | 77 | $1.04 \times 10^3$ | .... | $2.00 \times 10^5$ |
| Oxygen | 1·43 | 55 | 90 | $9.18 \times 10^2$ | .... | $2.40 \times 10^4$ |

The gas densities refer to a temperature of 273 K and a pressure of $1.01 \times 10^5$ Pa.

MARKS | DO NOT WRITE IN THIS MARGIN

**Total marks — 140 marks**

**Attempt ALL questions**

1.

Calvin Chan/shutterstock.com

A car on a long straight track accelerates from rest. The car's run begins at time $t = 0$.

Its velocity $v$ at time $t$ is given by the equation

$$v = 0 \cdot 135t^2 + 1 \cdot 26t$$

where $v$ is measured in $m\,s^{-1}$ and $t$ is measured in s.

Using **calculus** methods:

(a)  determine the acceleration of the car at $t = 15 \cdot 0\,s$;    3

*Space for working and answer*

(b)  determine the displacement of the car from its original position at this time.    3

*Space for working and answer*

MARKS | DO NOT WRITE IN THIS MARGIN

2.  (a)  An ideal conical pendulum consists of a mass moving with constant speed in a circular path, as shown in Figure 2A.

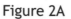

Figure 2A

(i)  Explain why the mass is accelerating despite moving with constant speed.    1

(ii)  State the direction of this acceleration.    1

2. **(continued)**

(b) Swingball is a garden game in which a ball is attached to a light string connected to a vertical pole as shown in Figure 2B.

The motion of the ball can be modelled as a conical pendulum.

The ball has a mass of 0·059 kg.

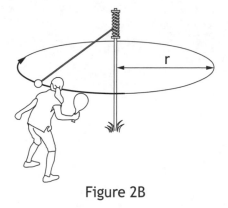

Figure 2B

(i) The ball is hit such that it moves with constant speed in a horizontal circle of radius 0·48 m.

The ball completes 1·5 revolutions in 2·69 s.

(A) Show that the angular velocity of the ball is 3·5 rad s⁻¹.    **2**

*Space for working and answer*

(B) Calculate the magnitude of the centripetal force acting on the ball.    **3**

*Space for working and answer*

MARKS | DO NOT WRITE IN THIS MARGIN

2.  (b)  (i)  (continued)

(C)  The horizontal component of the tension in the string provides this centripetal force and the vertical component balances the weight of the ball.

Calculate the magnitude of the tension in the string.        3

*Space for working and answer*

(ii)  The string breaks whilst the ball is at the position shown in Figure 2C.

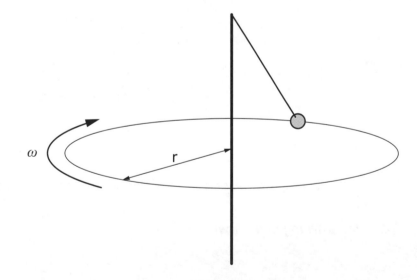

Figure 2C

On Figure 2C, draw the direction of the ball's velocity **immediately** after the string breaks.        1

(An additional diagram, if required, can be found on *Page thirty-nine*.)

MARKS | DO NOT WRITE IN THIS MARGIN

**3.** A spacecraft is orbiting a comet as shown in Figure 3.

The comet can be considered as a sphere with a radius of $2 \cdot 1 \times 10^3$ m and a mass of $9 \cdot 5 \times 10^{12}$ kg.

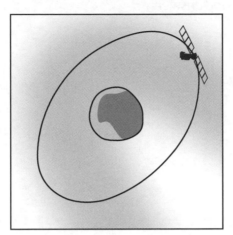

Figure 3 (not to scale)

(a) A lander was released by the spacecraft to land on the surface of the comet. After impact with the comet, the lander bounced back from the surface with an initial upward vertical velocity of $0 \cdot 38$ m s$^{-1}$.

By calculating the escape velocity of the comet, show that the lander returned to the surface for a second time.

*Space for working and answer*

4

**[Turn over**

MARKS | DO NOT WRITE IN THIS MARGIN

3.    (continued)

(b)    (i)    Show that the gravitational field strength at the surface of the comet is $1 \cdot 4 \times 10^{-4}\,\text{N kg}^{-1}$.

**3**

*Space for working and answer*

(ii)    Using the data from the space mission, a student tries to calculate the maximum height reached by the lander after its first bounce.

The student's working is shown below

$$v^2 = u^2 + 2as$$
$$0 = 0 \cdot 38^2 + 2 \times \left(-1 \cdot 4 \times 10^{-4}\right) \times s$$
$$s = 515 \cdot 7\,\text{m}$$

The actual maximum height reached by the lander was **not** as calculated by the student.

State whether the actual maximum height reached would be greater or smaller than calculated by the student.

You must justify your answer.

**3**

MARKS | DO NOT WRITE IN THIS MARGIN

4. Epsilon Eridani is a star $9.94 \times 10^{16}$ m from Earth. It has a diameter of $1.02 \times 10^{9}$ m. The apparent brightness of Epsilon Eridani is measured on Earth to be $1.05 \times 10^{-9}$ W m$^{-2}$.

  (a) Calculate the luminosity of Epsilon Eridani.

     *Space for working and answer*

    **3**

  (b) Calculate the surface temperature of Epsilon Eridani.

     *Space for working and answer*

    **3**

  (c) State an assumption made in your calculation in (b).

    **1**

[Turn over

MARKS | DO NOT WRITE IN THIS MARGIN

5. Einstein's theory of general relativity can be used to describe the motion of objects in non-inertial frames of reference. The equivalence principle is a key assumption of general relativity.

(a) Explain what is meant by the terms:

　　(i) *non-inertial frames of reference*;　　　　1

　　(ii) *the equivalence principle*.　　　　1

(b) Two astronauts are on board a spacecraft in deep space far away from any large masses. When the spacecraft is accelerating one astronaut throws a ball towards the other.

　　(i) On Figure 5A sketch the path that the ball would follow in the astronauts' frame of reference.　　　　1

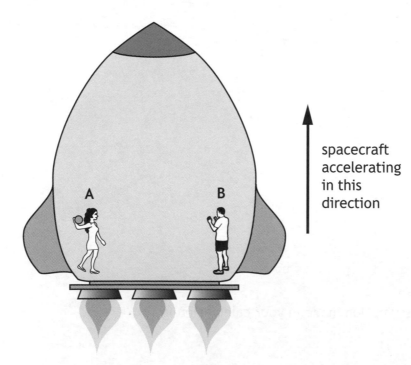

spacecraft accelerating in this direction

Figure 5A

(An additional diagram, if required, can be found on *Page thirty-nine*.)

MARKS | DO NOT WRITE IN THIS MARGIN

**5. (b) (continued)**

(ii) The experiment is repeated when the spacecraft is travelling at constant speed.

On Figure 5B sketch the path that the ball would follow in the astronauts' frame of reference.

1

spacecraft moving at a constant speed

Figure 5B

(An additional diagram, if required, can be found on *Page forty*.)

(c) A clock is on the surface of the Earth and an identical clock is on board a spacecraft which is accelerating in deep space at $8\,\mathrm{m\,s^{-2}}$.

State which clock runs slower.

Justify your answer in terms of the equivalence principle.

2

**[Turn over**

MARKS | DO NOT WRITE IN THIS MARGIN

6. A student makes the following statement.

"Quantum theory — I don't understand it. I don't really know what it is. I believe that classical physics can explain everything."

Use your knowledge of physics to comment on the statement.    3

MARKS | DO NOT WRITE IN THIS MARGIN

7.  (a)  The Earth can be modelled as a black body radiator.

The average surface temperature of the Earth can be estimated using the relationship

$$T = \frac{b}{\lambda_{peak}}$$

where

$T$ is the average surface temperature of the Earth in kelvin;

$b$ is Wien's Displacement Constant equal to $2 \cdot 89 \times 10^{-3}\,K\,m$;

$\lambda_{peak}$ is the peak wavelength of the radiation emitted by a black body radiator.

The average surface temperature of Earth is 15 °C.

(i)  Estimate the peak wavelength of the radiation emitted by Earth.    3

*Space for working and answer*

(ii)  To which part of the electromagnetic spectrum does this peak wavelength correspond?    1

**[Turn over**

**7. (continued)**

(b) In order to investigate the properties of black body radiators a student makes measurements from the spectra produced by a filament lamp. Measurements are made when the lamp is operated at its rated voltage and when it is operated at a lower voltage.

The filament lamp can be considered to be a black body radiator.

A graph of the results obtained is shown in Figure 7.

Figure 7

(i) State which curve corresponds to the radiation emitted when the filament lamp is operating at its rated voltage.

You must justify your answer.

2

(ii) The shape of the curves on the graph on Figure 7 is not as predicted by classical physics.

On Figure 7, sketch a curve to show the result predicted by classical physics.

1

(An additional graph, if required, can be found on *Page forty*.)

MARKS | DO NOT WRITE IN THIS MARGIN

8. Werner Heisenberg is considered to be one of the pioneers of quantum mechanics.

He is most famous for his uncertainty principle which can be expressed in the equation

$$\Delta x \Delta p_x \geq \frac{h}{4\pi}$$

(a)  (i)  State what quantity is represented by the term $\Delta p_x$.　　1

　　(ii)  Explain the implications of the Heisenberg uncertainty principle for experimental measurements.　　1

[Turn over

8. **(continued)**

(b) In an experiment to investigate the nature of particles, individual electrons were fired one at a time from an electron gun through a narrow double slit. The position where each electron struck the detector was recorded and displayed on a computer screen.

The experiment continued until a clear pattern emerged on the screen as shown in Figure 8.

The momentum of each electron at the double slit is $6 \cdot 5 \times 10^{-24}\,\text{kg m s}^{-1}$.

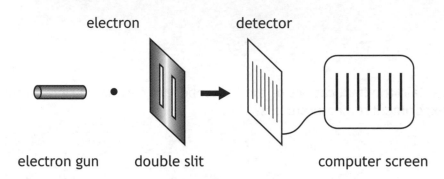

electron          detector

electron gun      double slit                    computer screen

Figure 8                    not to scale

(i) The experimenter had three different double slits with slit separations $0 \cdot 1\,\text{mm}$, $0 \cdot 1\,\mu\text{m}$ and $0 \cdot 1\,\text{nm}$.

State which double slit was used to produce the image on the screen.

You must justify your answer by calculation of the de Broglie wavelength.

**4**

*Space for working and answer*

MARKS | DO NOT WRITE IN THIS MARGIN

8.   (b)   (continued)

(ii)   The uncertainty in the momentum of an electron at the double slit is $6\cdot5 \times 10^{-26}\,\text{kg}\,\text{m}\,\text{s}^{-1}$.

Calculate the minimum absolute uncertainty in the position of the electron.

3

*Space for working and answer*

(iii)   Explain fully how the experimental result shown in Figure 8 can be interpreted.

3

[Turn over

9.  A particle with charge $q$ and mass $m$ is travelling with constant speed $v$. The particle enters a uniform magnetic field at 90° and is forced to move in a circle of radius $r$ as shown in Figure 9.

    The magnetic induction of the field is $B$.

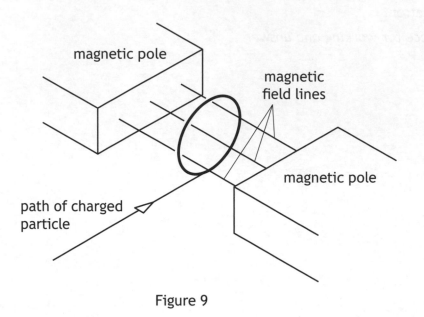

magnetic pole

magnetic field lines

magnetic pole

path of charged particle

Figure 9

(a)  Show that the radius of the circular path of the particle is given by

$$r = \frac{mv}{Bq}$$

2

MARKS | DO NOT WRITE IN THIS MARGIN

9.  **(continued)**

(b)  In an experimental nuclear reactor, charged particles are contained in a magnetic field. One such particle is a deuteron consisting of one proton and one neutron.

The kinetic energy of each deuteron is 1·50 MeV.

The mass of the deuteron is $3\cdot34 \times 10^{-27}$ kg.

Relativistic effects can be ignored.

(i)  Calculate the speed of the deuteron.    **4**

*Space for working and answer*

(ii)  Calculate the magnetic induction required to keep the deuteron moving in a circular path of radius 2·50 m.    **2**

*Space for working and answer*

[Turn over

**9. (b) (continued)**

(iii) Deuterons are fused together in the reactor to produce isotopes of helium.

$^3_2$He nuclei, each comprising 2 protons and 1 neutron, are present in the reactor.

A $^3_2$He nucleus also moves in a circular path in the same magnetic field.

The $^3_2$He nucleus moves at the same speed as the deuteron.

State whether the radius of the circular path of the $^3_2$He nucleus is greater than, equal to or less than 2·50 m.

You must justify your answer.

**2**

MARKS | DO NOT WRITE IN THIS MARGIN

10. (a) (i) State what is meant by *simple harmonic motion*.    **1**

(ii) The displacement of an oscillating object can be described by the expression

$$y = A\cos\omega t$$

where the symbols have their usual meaning.

Show that this expression is a solution to the equation

$$\frac{d^2 y}{dt^2} + \omega^2 y = 0$$

**2**

[Turn over

## 10. (continued)

(b) A mass of 1·5 kg is suspended from a spring of negligible mass as shown in Figure 10. The mass is displaced downwards 0·040 m from its equilibrium position.

The mass is then released from this position and begins to oscillate. The mass completes ten oscillations in a time of 12 s.

Frictional forces can be considered to be negligible.

Figure 10

(i) Show that the angular frequency $\omega$ of the mass is $5 \cdot 2 \, \text{rad s}^{-1}$.    **3**

*Space for working and answer*

(ii) Calculate the maximum velocity of the mass.    **3**

*Space for working and answer*

MARKS | DO NOT WRITE IN THIS MARGIN

10. **(b) (continued)**

(iii) Determine the potential energy stored in the spring when the mass is at its maximum displacement.    **3**

*Space for working and answer*

(c) The system is now modified so that a damping force acts on the oscillating mass.

(i) Describe how this modification may be achieved.    **1**

(ii) Using the axes below sketch a graph showing, for the modified system, how the displacement of the mass varies with time after release.

Numerical values are **not** required on the axes.    **1**

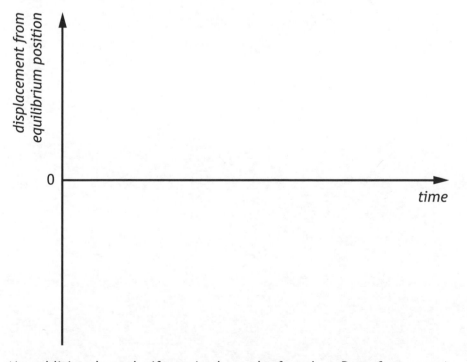

(An additional graph, if required, can be found on *Page forty-one*.)

**[Turn over**

MARKS | DO NOT WRITE IN THIS MARGIN

11.

foghorn

A ship emits a blast of sound from its foghorn. The sound wave is described by the equation

$$y = 0{\cdot}250 \sin 2\pi\left(118t - 0{\cdot}357x\right)$$

where the symbols have their usual meaning.

(a)  Determine the speed of the sound wave.    **4**

*Space for working and answer*

MARKS | DO NOT WRITE IN THIS MARGIN

**11. (continued)**

(b) The sound from the ship's foghorn reflects from a cliff. When it reaches the ship this reflected sound has half the energy of the original sound.

Write an equation describing the reflected sound wave at this point.  **4**

**[Turn over**

12. Some early 3D video cameras recorded two separate images at the same time to create two almost identical movies.

Cinemas showed 3D films by projecting these two images simultaneously onto the same screen using two projectors. Each projector had a polarising filter through which the light passed as shown in Figure 12.

polarising filters

to cinema screen

film projectors

Figure 12

(a) Describe how the transmission axes of the two polarising filters should be arranged so that the two images on the screen do not interfere with each other.

1

(b) A student watches a 3D movie using a pair of glasses which contains two polarising filters, one for each eye.

Explain how this arrangement enables a different image to be seen by each eye.

2

12.    **(continued)**

(c)    Before the film starts, the student looks at a ceiling lamp through one of the filters in the glasses. While looking at the lamp, the student then rotates the filter through 90°.

State what effect, if any, this rotation will have on the observed brightness of the lamp.

Justify your answer.    **2**

(d)    During the film, the student looks at the screen through only one of the filters in the glasses. The student then rotates the filter through 90° and does not observe any change in brightness.

Explain this observation.    **1**

**[Turn over**

MARKS | DO NOT WRITE IN THIS MARGIN

**13.** (a) $Q_1$ is a point charge of +12 nC. Point Y is 0·30 m from $Q_1$ as shown in Figure 13A.

+12 nC           Y

$Q_1$ •

•

0·30 m

Figure 13A

Show that the electrical potential at point Y is +360 V.

*Space for working and answer*

2

(b) A second point charge $Q_2$ is placed at a distance of 0·40 m from point Y as shown in Figure 13B. The electrical potential at point Y is now zero.

+12 nC          Y

$Q_1$ •        •        • $Q_2$

0·30 m        0·40 m

Figure 13B

(i) Determine the charge of $Q_2$.

*Space for working and answer*

3

MARKS | DO NOT WRITE IN THIS MARGIN

**13.** **(b)** **(continued)**

(ii) Determine the electric field strength at point Y.    4

*Space for working and answer*

(iii) On Figure 13C, sketch the electric field pattern for this system of charges.    2

$Q_1$ •                                                    • $Q_2$

Figure 13C

(An additional diagram, if required, can be found on *Page forty-one.*)

**[Turn over**

MARKS | DO NOT WRITE IN THIS MARGIN

**14.** A student measures the magnetic induction at a distance $r$ from a long straight current carrying wire using the apparatus shown in Figure 14.

Figure 14

The following data are obtained.

Distance from wire $r = 0.10$ m
Magnetic induction $B = 5.0$ μT

(a) Use the data to calculate the current $I$ in the wire.    **3**

*Space for working and answer*

(b) The student estimates the following uncertainties in the measurements of $B$ and $r$.

| Uncertainties in $r$ | | Uncertainties in $B$ | |
|---|---|---|---|
| reading | ±0.002 m | reading | ±0.1 μT |
| calibration | ±0.0005 m | calibration | ±1.5% of reading |

   (i) Calculate the percentage uncertainty in the measurement of $r$.    **1**

     *Space for working and answer*

MARKS | DO NOT WRITE IN THIS MARGIN

14. (b) (continued)

(ii) Calculate the percentage uncertainty in the measurement of $B$. **3**

*Space for working and answer*

(iii) Calculate the absolute uncertainty in the value of the current in the wire. **2**

*Space for working and answer*

(c) The student measures distance $r$, as shown in Figure 14, using a metre stick. The smallest scale division on the metre stick is 1 mm.

Suggest a reason why the student's estimate of the reading uncertainty in $r$ is not $\pm 0\cdot 5$ mm. **1**

[Turn over

15. A student constructs a simple air-insulated capacitor using two parallel metal plates, each of area A, separated by a distance $d$. The plates are separated using small insulating spacers as shown in Figure 15A.

capacitance meter

**Figure 15A**

The capacitance $C$ of the capacitor is given by

$$C = \varepsilon_0 \frac{A}{d}$$

The student investigates how the capacitance depends on the separation of the plates. The student uses a capacitance meter to measure the capacitance for different plate separations. The plate separation is measured using a ruler.

The results are used to plot the graph shown in Figure 15B.

The area of each metal plate is $9 \cdot 0 \times 10^{-2}\,\mathrm{m^2}$.

**Figure 15B**

MARKS | DO NOT WRITE IN THIS MARGIN

15.    (continued)

(a)    (i)    Use information from the graph to determine a value for $\varepsilon_o$, the permittivity of free space.    3

*Space for working and answer*

(ii)    Use your calculated value for the permittivity of free space to determine a value for the speed of light in air.    3

*Space for working and answer*

(b)    The best fit line on the graph does not pass through the origin as theory predicts.

Suggest a reason for this.    1

**[Turn over**

[BLANK PAGE]

DO NOT WRITE ON THIS PAGE

MARKS | DO NOT WRITE IN THIS MARGIN

16. A student uses two methods to determine the moment of inertia of a solid sphere about an axis through its centre.

(a) In the first method the student measures the mass of the sphere to be 3·8 kg and the radius to be 0·053 m.

Calculate the moment of inertia of the sphere.    **3**

*Space for working and answer*

(b) In the second method, the student uses conservation of energy to determine the moment of inertia of the sphere.

The following equation describes the conservation of energy as the sphere rolls down the slope

$$mgh = \frac{1}{2}mv^2 + \frac{1}{2}I\omega^2$$

where the symbols have their usual meanings.

The equation can be rearranged to give the following expression

$$2gh = \left(\frac{I}{mr^2} + 1\right)v^2$$

This expression is in the form of the equation of a straight line through the origin,

$$y = gradient \times x$$

[Turn over

16. (b) (continued)

The student measures the height of the slope $h$. The student then allows the sphere to roll down the slope and measures the final speed of the sphere $v$ at the bottom of the slope as shown in Figure 16.

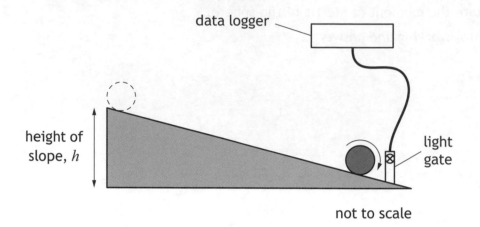

Figure 16

The following is an extract from the student's notebook.

| $h$ (m) | $v$ (m s$^{-1}$) | $2gh$ (m$^2$ s$^{-2}$) | $v^2$ (m$^2$ s$^{-2}$) |
|---------|---------|---------|---------|
| 0·020 | 0·42 | 0·39 | 0·18 |
| 0·040 | 0·63 | 0·78 | 0·40 |
| 0·060 | 0·68 | 1·18 | 0·46 |
| 0·080 | 0·95 | 1·57 | 0·90 |
| 0·100 | 1·05 | 1·96 | 1·10 |

$m = 3\cdot8\,\text{kg}$     $r = 0\cdot053\,\text{m}$

(i) On the square-ruled paper on *Page thirty-seven*, draw a graph that would allow the student to determine the moment of inertia of the sphere. **3**

(ii) Use the gradient of your line to determine the moment of inertia of the sphere. **3**

*Space for working and answer*

(An additional square-ruled paper, if required, can be found on *Page forty-two*.)

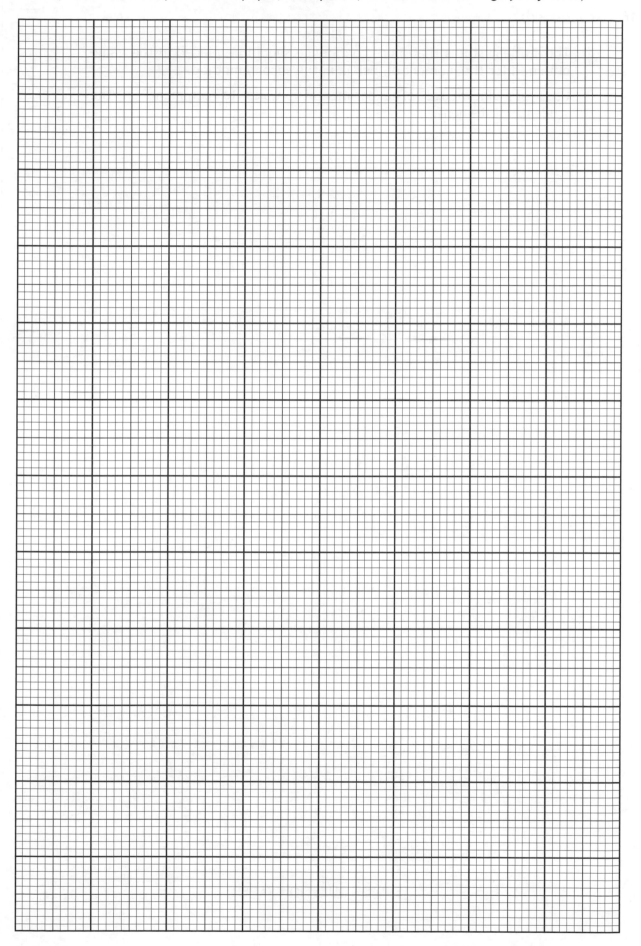

**[Turn over for next question**

MARKS | DO NOT WRITE IN THIS MARGIN

**16.**    **(continued)**

    (c)   The student states that more confidence should be placed in the value obtained for the moment of inertia in the second method.

        Use your knowledge of experimental physics to comment on the student's statement.

    3

**[END OF QUESTION PAPER]**

## ADDITIONAL SPACE FOR ANSWERS AND ROUGH WORK

Additional diagram for Question 2 (b) (ii)

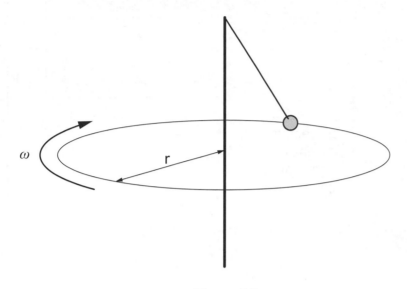

Figure 2C

Additional diagram for Question 5 (b) (i)

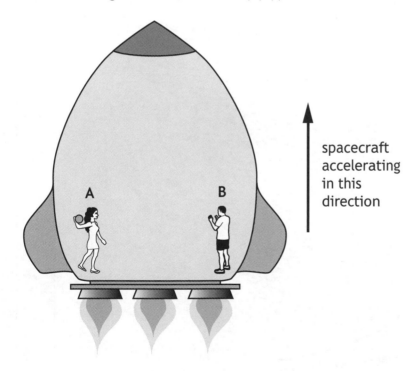

spacecraft accelerating in this direction

Figure 5A

## ADDITIONAL SPACE FOR ANSWERS AND ROUGH WORK

Additional diagram for Question 5 (b) (ii)

spacecraft moving at a constant speed

Figure 5B

Additional diagram for Question 7 (b) (ii)

Figure 7

## ADDITIONAL SPACE FOR ANSWERS AND ROUGH WORK

Additional diagram for Question 10 (c) (ii)

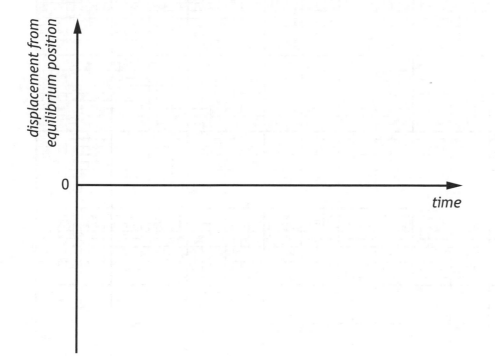

Additional diagram for Question 13 (b) (iii)

$Q_1$ •                                    • $Q_2$

Figure 13C

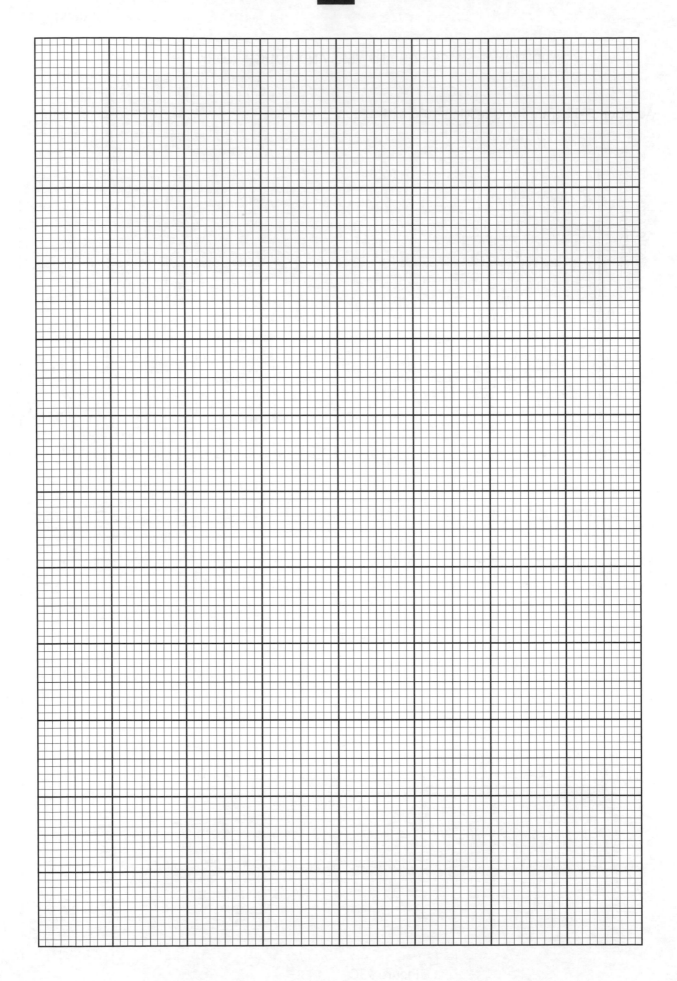

**MARKS** | DO NOT WRITE IN THIS MARGIN

ADDITIONAL SPACE FOR ANSWERS AND ROUGH WORK

**ADDITIONAL SPACE FOR ANSWERS AND ROUGH WORK**

# ADVANCED HIGHER

# 2017

National
Qualifications
2017

**X757/77/11**

**Physics**
**Relationships Sheet**

WEDNESDAY, 17 MAY
9:00 AM — 11:30 AM

# Relationships required for Physics Advanced Higher

$$v = \frac{ds}{dt}$$

$$a = \frac{dv}{dt} = \frac{d^2s}{dt^2}$$

$$v = u + at$$

$$s = ut + \frac{1}{2}at^2$$

$$v^2 = u^2 + 2as$$

$$\omega = \frac{d\theta}{dt}$$

$$\alpha = \frac{d\omega}{dt} = \frac{d^2\theta}{dt^2}$$

$$\omega = \omega_o + \alpha t$$

$$\theta = \omega_o t + \frac{1}{2}\alpha t^2$$

$$\omega^2 = \omega_o^2 + 2\alpha\theta$$

$$s = r\theta$$

$$v = r\omega$$

$$a_t = r\alpha$$

$$a_r = \frac{v^2}{r} = r\omega^2$$

$$F = \frac{mv^2}{r} = mr\omega^2$$

$$T = Fr$$

$$T = I\alpha$$

$$L = mvr = mr^2\omega$$

$$L = I\omega$$

$$E_K = \frac{1}{2}I\omega^2$$

$$F = G\frac{Mm}{r^2}$$

$$V = -\frac{GM}{r}$$

$$v = \sqrt{\frac{2GM}{r}}$$

apparent brightness, $b = \dfrac{L}{4\pi r^2}$

Power per unit area $= \sigma T^4$

$$L = 4\pi r^2 \sigma T^4$$

$$r_{Schwarzschild} = \frac{2GM}{c^2}$$

$$E = hf$$

$$\lambda = \frac{h}{p}$$

$$mvr = \frac{nh}{2\pi}$$

$$\Delta x\,\Delta p_x \geq \frac{h}{4\pi}$$

$$\Delta E\,\Delta t \geq \frac{h}{4\pi}$$

$$F = qvB$$

$$\omega = 2\pi f$$

$$a = \frac{d^2y}{dt^2} = -\omega^2 y$$

$y = A\cos\omega t$  or  $y = A\sin\omega t$

$v = \pm\omega\sqrt{(A^2 - y^2)}$

$E_K = \frac{1}{2}m\omega^2(A^2 - y^2)$

$E_P = \frac{1}{2}m\omega^2 y^2$

$y = A\sin 2\pi(ft - \frac{x}{\lambda})$

$E = kA^2$

$\phi = \frac{2\pi x}{\lambda}$

optical path difference $= m\lambda$  or  $\left(m+\frac{1}{2}\right)\lambda$

where $m = 0, 1, 2....$

$\Delta x = \frac{\lambda l}{2d}$

$d = \frac{\lambda}{4n}$

$\Delta x = \frac{\lambda D}{d}$

$n = \tan i_P$

$F = \frac{Q_1 Q_2}{4\pi\varepsilon_o r^2}$

$E = \frac{Q}{4\pi\varepsilon_o r^2}$

$V = \frac{Q}{4\pi\varepsilon_o r}$

$F = QE$

$V = Ed$

$F = IlB\sin\theta$

$B = \frac{\mu_o I}{2\pi r}$

$c = \frac{1}{\sqrt{\varepsilon_o \mu_o}}$

$t = RC$

$X_C = \frac{V}{I}$

$X_C = \frac{1}{2\pi fC}$

$\varepsilon = -L\frac{dI}{dt}$

$E = \frac{1}{2}LI^2$

$X_L = \frac{V}{I}$

$X_L = 2\pi fL$

$\frac{\Delta W}{W} = \sqrt{\left(\frac{\Delta X}{X}\right)^2 + \left(\frac{\Delta Y}{Y}\right)^2 + \left(\frac{\Delta Z}{Z}\right)^2}$

$\Delta W = \sqrt{\Delta X^2 + \Delta Y^2 + \Delta Z^2}$

$d = \bar{v}t$

$s = \bar{v}t$

$v = u + at$

$s = ut + \dfrac{1}{2}at^2$

$v^2 = u^2 + 2as$

$s = \dfrac{1}{2}(u+v)t$

$W = mg$

$F = ma$

$E_W = Fd$

$E_P = mgh$

$E_K = \dfrac{1}{2}mv^2$

$P = \dfrac{E}{t}$

$p = mv$

$Ft = mv - mu$

$F = G\dfrac{Mm}{r^2}$

$t' = \dfrac{t}{\sqrt{1-\left(v/c\right)^2}}$

$l' = l\sqrt{1-\left(v/c\right)^2}$

$f_o = f_s\left(\dfrac{v}{v \pm v_s}\right)$

$z = \dfrac{\lambda_{observed} - \lambda_{rest}}{\lambda_{rest}}$

$z = \dfrac{v}{c}$

$v = H_0 d$

$W = QV$

$E = mc^2$

$E = hf$

$E_K = hf - hf_0$

$E_2 - E_1 = hf$

$T = \dfrac{1}{f}$

$v = f\lambda$

$d\sin\theta = m\lambda$

$n = \dfrac{\sin\theta_1}{\sin\theta_2}$

$\dfrac{\sin\theta_1}{\sin\theta_2} = \dfrac{\lambda_1}{\lambda_2} = \dfrac{v_1}{v_2}$

$\sin\theta_c = \dfrac{1}{n}$

$I = \dfrac{k}{d^2}$

$I = \dfrac{P}{A}$

$V_{peak} = \sqrt{2}V_{rms}$

$I_{peak} = \sqrt{2}I_{rms}$

$Q = It$

$V = IR$

$P = IV = I^2R = \dfrac{V^2}{R}$

$R_T = R_1 + R_2 + ....$

$\dfrac{1}{R_T} = \dfrac{1}{R_1} + \dfrac{1}{R_2} + ....$

$E = V + Ir$

$V_1 = \left(\dfrac{R_1}{R_1 + R_2}\right)V_s$

$\dfrac{V_1}{V_2} = \dfrac{R_1}{R_2}$

$C = \dfrac{Q}{V}$

$E = \dfrac{1}{2}QV = \dfrac{1}{2}CV^2 = \dfrac{1}{2}\dfrac{Q^2}{C}$

path difference $= m\lambda$   or   $\left(m+\dfrac{1}{2}\right)\lambda$   where $m = 0,1,2...$

random uncertainty $= \dfrac{\text{max. value} - \text{min. value}}{\text{number of values}}$

# Additional Relationships

## Circle

circumference $= 2\pi r$

area $= \pi r^2$

## Sphere

area $= 4\pi r^2$

volume $= \frac{4}{3}\pi r^3$

## Trigonometry

$\sin\theta = \dfrac{\text{opposite}}{\text{hypotenuse}}$

$\cos\theta = \dfrac{\text{adjacent}}{\text{hypotenuse}}$

$\tan\theta = \dfrac{\text{opposite}}{\text{adjacent}}$

$\sin^2\theta + \cos^2\theta = 1$

## Moment of inertia

point mass
$I = mr^2$

rod about centre
$I = \frac{1}{12}ml^2$

rod about end
$I = \frac{1}{3}ml^2$

disc about centre
$I = \frac{1}{2}mr^2$

sphere about centre
$I = \frac{2}{5}mr^2$

## Table of standard derivatives

| $f(x)$ | $f'(x)$ |
|--------|---------|
| $\sin ax$ | $a\cos ax$ |
| $\cos ax$ | $-a\sin ax$ |

## Table of standard integrals

| $f(x)$ | $\int f(x)dx$ |
|--------|---------------|
| $\sin ax$ | $-\dfrac{1}{a}\cos ax + C$ |
| $\cos ax$ | $\dfrac{1}{a}\sin ax + C$ |

# Electron Arrangements of Elements

**Key**

| Atomic number |
| Symbol |
| Electron arrangement |
| Name |

## Main Groups

| Group 1 (1) | Group 2 (2) | Group 0 (18) |
|---|---|---|
| 1 **H** 1 Hydrogen | | 2 **He** 2 Helium |
| 3 **Li** 2,1 Lithium | 4 **Be** 2,2 Beryllium | |
| 11 **Na** 2,8,1 Sodium | 12 **Mg** 2,8,2 Magnesium | |
| 19 **K** 2,8,8,1 Potassium | 20 **Ca** 2,8,8,2 Calcium | |
| 37 **Rb** 2,8,18,8,1 Rubidium | 38 **Sr** 2,8,18,8,2 Strontium | |
| 55 **Cs** 2,8,18,18,8,1 Caesium | 56 **Ba** 2,8,18,18,8,2 Barium | |
| 87 **Fr** 2,8,18,32,18,8,1 Francium | 88 **Ra** 2,8,18,32,18,8,2 Radium | |

## Transition Elements

| (3) | (4) | (5) | (6) | (7) | (8) | (9) | (10) | (11) | (12) |
|---|---|---|---|---|---|---|---|---|---|
| 21 **Sc** 2,8,9,2 Scandium | 22 **Ti** 2,8,10,2 Titanium | 23 **V** 2,8,11,2 Vanadium | 24 **Cr** 2,8,13,1 Chromium | 25 **Mn** 2,8,13,2 Manganese | 26 **Fe** 2,8,14,2 Iron | 27 **Co** 2,8,15,2 Cobalt | 28 **Ni** 2,8,16,2 Nickel | 29 **Cu** 2,8,18,1 Copper | 30 **Zn** 2,8,18,2 Zinc |
| 39 **Y** 2,8,18,9,2 Yttrium | 40 **Zr** 2,8,18,10,2 Zirconium | 41 **Nb** 2,8,18,12,1 Niobium | 42 **Mo** 2,8,18,13,1 Molybdenum | 43 **Tc** 2,8,18,13,2 Technetium | 44 **Ru** 2,8,18,15,1 Ruthenium | 45 **Rh** 2,8,18,16,1 Rhodium | 46 **Pd** 2,8,18,18,0 Palladium | 47 **Ag** 2,8,18,18,1 Silver | 48 **Cd** 2,8,18,18,2 Cadmium |
| 57 **La** 2,8,18,18,9,2 Lanthanum | 72 **Hf** 2,8,18,32,10,2 Hafnium | 73 **Ta** 2,8,18,32,11,2 Tantalum | 74 **W** 2,8,18,32,12,2 Tungsten | 75 **Re** 2,8,18,32,13,2 Rhenium | 76 **Os** 2,8,18,32,14,2 Osmium | 77 **Ir** 2,8,18,32,15,2 Iridium | 78 **Pt** 2,8,18,32,17,1 Platinum | 79 **Au** 2,8,18,32,18,1 Gold | 80 **Hg** 2,8,18,32,18,2 Mercury |
| 89 **Ac** 2,8,18,32,18,9,2 Actinium | 104 **Rf** 2,8,18,32,32,10,2 Rutherfordium | 105 **Db** 2,8,18,32,32,11,2 Dubnium | 106 **Sg** 2,8,18,32,32,12,2 Seaborgium | 107 **Bh** 2,8,18,32,32,13,2 Bohrium | 108 **Hs** 2,8,18,32,32,14,2 Hassium | 109 **Mt** 2,8,18,32,32,15,2 Meitnerium | 110 **Ds** 2,8,18,32,32,17,1 Darmstadtium | 111 **Rg** 2,8,18,32,32,18,1 Roentgenium | 112 **Cn** 2,8,18,32,32,18,2 Copernicium |

## Groups 3–0

| Group 3 (13) | Group 4 (14) | Group 5 (15) | Group 6 (16) | Group 7 (17) |
|---|---|---|---|---|
| 5 **B** 2,3 Boron | 6 **C** 2,4 Carbon | 7 **N** 2,5 Nitrogen | 8 **O** 2,6 Oxygen | 9 **F** 2,7 Fluorine |
| 13 **Al** 2,8,3 Aluminium | 14 **Si** 2,8,4 Silicon | 15 **P** 2,8,5 Phosphorus | 16 **S** 2,8,6 Sulfur | 17 **Cl** 2,8,7 Chlorine |
| 31 **Ga** 2,8,18,3 Gallium | 32 **Ge** 2,8,18,4 Germanium | 33 **As** 2,8,18,5 Arsenic | 34 **Se** 2,8,18,6 Selenium | 35 **Br** 2,8,18,7 Bromine |
| 49 **In** 2,8,18,18,3 Indium | 50 **Sn** 2,8,18,18,4 Tin | 51 **Sb** 2,8,18,18,5 Antimony | 52 **Te** 2,8,18,18,6 Tellurium | 53 **I** 2,8,18,18,7 Iodine |
| 81 **Tl** 2,8,18,32,18,3 Thallium | 82 **Pb** 2,8,18,32,18,4 Lead | 83 **Bi** 2,8,18,32,18,5 Bismuth | 84 **Po** 2,8,18,32,18,6 Polonium | 85 **At** 2,8,18,32,18,7 Astatine |

(Group 0: 10 **Ne** 2,8 Neon; 18 **Ar** 2,8,8 Argon; 36 **Kr** 2,8,18,8 Krypton; 54 **Xe** 2,8,18,18,8 Xenon; 86 **Rn** 2,8,18,32,18,8 Radon)

## Lanthanides

| 57 **La** 2,8,18,18,9,2 Lanthanum | 58 **Ce** 2,8,18,20,8,2 Cerium | 59 **Pr** 2,8,18,21,8,2 Praseodymium | 60 **Nd** 2,8,18,22,8,2 Neodymium | 61 **Pm** 2,8,18,23,8,2 Promethium | 62 **Sm** 2,8,18,24,8,2 Samarium | 63 **Eu** 2,8,18,25,8,2 Europium | 64 **Gd** 2,8,18,25,9,2 Gadolinium | 65 **Tb** 2,8,18,27,8,2 Terbium | 66 **Dy** 2,8,18,28,8,2 Dysprosium | 67 **Ho** 2,8,18,29,8,2 Holmium | 68 **Er** 2,8,18,30,8,2 Erbium | 69 **Tm** 2,8,18,31,8,2 Thulium | 70 **Yb** 2,8,18,32,8,2 Ytterbium | 71 **Lu** 2,8,18,32,9,2 Lutetium |
|---|---|---|---|---|---|---|---|---|---|---|---|---|---|---|

## Actinides

| 89 **Ac** 2,8,18,32,18,9,2 Actinium | 90 **Th** 2,8,18,32,18,10,2 Thorium | 91 **Pa** 2,8,18,32,20,9,2 Protactinium | 92 **U** 2,8,18,32,21,9,2 Uranium | 93 **Np** 2,8,18,32,22,9,2 Neptunium | 94 **Pu** 2,8,18,32,24,8,2 Plutonium | 95 **Am** 2,8,18,32,25,8,2 Americium | 96 **Cm** 2,8,18,32,25,9,2 Curium | 97 **Bk** 2,8,18,32,27,8,2 Berkelium | 98 **Cf** 2,8,18,32,28,8,2 Californium | 99 **Es** 2,8,18,32,29,8,2 Einsteinium | 100 **Fm** 2,8,18,32,30,8,2 Fermium | 101 **Md** 2,8,18,32,31,8,2 Mendelevium | 102 **No** 2,8,18,32,32,8,2 Nobelium | 103 **Lr** 2,8,18,32,32,9,2 Lawrencium |
|---|---|---|---|---|---|---|---|---|---|---|---|---|---|---|

[BLANK PAGE]

DO NOT WRITE ON THIS PAGE

[BLANK PAGE]

DO NOT WRITE ON THIS PAGE

# AH

National
Qualifications
2017

Mark

**X757/77/01**

**Physics**

WEDNESDAY, 17 MAY

9:00 AM — 11:30 AM

**Fill in these boxes and read what is printed below.**

Full name of centre

Town

Forename(s)

Surname

Number of seat

Date of birth

| Day | Month | Year | Scottish candidate number |
|-----|-------|------|---------------------------|

**Total marks — 140**

Attempt ALL questions.

Reference may be made to the Physics Relationship Sheet X757/77/11 and the Data Sheet on *Page two*.

Write your answers clearly in the spaces provided in this booklet. Additional space for answers and rough work is provided at the end of this booklet. If you use this space you must clearly identify the question number you are attempting. Any rough work must be written in this booklet. You should score through your rough work when you have written your final copy.

Care should be taken to give an appropriate number of significant figures in the final answers to calculations.

Use **blue** or **black** ink.

Before leaving the examination room you must give this booklet to the Invigilator; if you do not, you may lose all the marks for this paper.

## DATA SHEET

COMMON PHYSICAL QUANTITIES

| Quantity | Symbol | Value | Quantity | Symbol | Value |
|---|---|---|---|---|---|
| Gravitational acceleration on Earth | $g$ | $9{\cdot}8\,\mathrm{m\,s^{-2}}$ | Mass of electron | $m_e$ | $9{\cdot}11 \times 10^{-31}\,\mathrm{kg}$ |
| Radius of Earth | $R_E$ | $6{\cdot}4 \times 10^6\,\mathrm{m}$ | Charge on electron | $e$ | $-1{\cdot}60 \times 10^{-19}\,\mathrm{C}$ |
| Mass of Earth | $M_E$ | $6{\cdot}0 \times 10^{24}\,\mathrm{kg}$ | Mass of neutron | $m_n$ | $1{\cdot}675 \times 10^{-27}\,\mathrm{kg}$ |
| Mass of Moon | $M_M$ | $7{\cdot}3 \times 10^{22}\,\mathrm{kg}$ | Mass of proton | $m_p$ | $1{\cdot}673 \times 10^{-27}\,\mathrm{kg}$ |
| Radius of Moon | $R_M$ | $1{\cdot}7 \times 10^6\,\mathrm{m}$ | Mass of alpha particle | $m_\alpha$ | $6{\cdot}645 \times 10^{-27}\,\mathrm{kg}$ |
| Mean Radius of Moon Orbit | | $3{\cdot}84 \times 10^8\,\mathrm{m}$ | Charge on alpha particle | | $3{\cdot}20 \times 10^{-19}\,\mathrm{C}$ |
| Solar radius | | $6{\cdot}955 \times 10^8\,\mathrm{m}$ | Planck's constant | $h$ | $6{\cdot}63 \times 10^{-34}\,\mathrm{J\,s}$ |
| Mass of Sun | | $2{\cdot}0 \times 10^{30}\,\mathrm{kg}$ | Permittivity of free space | $\varepsilon_0$ | $8{\cdot}85 \times 10^{-12}\,\mathrm{F\,m^{-1}}$ |
| 1 AU | | $1{\cdot}5 \times 10^{11}\,\mathrm{m}$ | Permeability of free space | $\mu_0$ | $4\pi \times 10^{-7}\,\mathrm{H\,m^{-1}}$ |
| Stefan-Boltzmann constant | $\sigma$ | $5{\cdot}67 \times 10^{-8}\,\mathrm{W\,m^{-2}\,K^{-4}}$ | Speed of light in vacuum | $c$ | $3{\cdot}00 \times 10^8\,\mathrm{m\,s^{-1}}$ |
| Universal constant of gravitation | $G$ | $6{\cdot}67 \times 10^{-11}\,\mathrm{m^3\,kg^{-1}\,s^{-2}}$ | Speed of sound in air | $v$ | $3{\cdot}4 \times 10^2\,\mathrm{m\,s^{-1}}$ |

REFRACTIVE INDICES

The refractive indices refer to sodium light of wavelength 589 nm and to substances at a temperature of 273 K.

| Substance | Refractive index | Substance | Refractive index |
|---|---|---|---|
| Diamond | 2·42 | Glycerol | 1·47 |
| Glass | 1·51 | Water | 1·33 |
| Ice | 1·31 | Air | 1·00 |
| Perspex | 1·49 | Magnesium Fluoride | 1·38 |

SPECTRAL LINES

| Element | Wavelength/nm | Colour | Element | Wavelength/nm | Colour |
|---|---|---|---|---|---|
| Hydrogen | 656 | Red | Cadmium | 644 | Red |
| | 486 | Blue-green | | 509 | Green |
| | 434 | Blue-violet | | 480 | Blue |
| | 410 | Violet | | Lasers | |
| | 397 | Ultraviolet | Element | Wavelength/nm | Colour |
| | 389 | Ultraviolet | Carbon dioxide | 9550 $\big\}$ 10 590 | Infrared |
| Sodium | 589 | Yellow | Helium-neon | 633 | Red |

PROPERTIES OF SELECTED MATERIALS

| Substance | Density/ $\mathrm{kg\,m^{-3}}$ | Melting Point/ K | Boiling Point/K | Specific Heat Capacity/ $\mathrm{J\,kg^{-1}\,K^{-1}}$ | Specific Latent Heat of Fusion/ $\mathrm{J\,kg^{-1}}$ | Specific Latent Heat of Vaporisation/ $\mathrm{J\,kg^{-1}}$ |
|---|---|---|---|---|---|---|
| Aluminium | $2{\cdot}70 \times 10^3$ | 933 | 2623 | $9{\cdot}02 \times 10^2$ | $3{\cdot}95 \times 10^5$ | . . . . |
| Copper | $8{\cdot}96 \times 10^3$ | 1357 | 2853 | $3{\cdot}86 \times 10^2$ | $2{\cdot}05 \times 10^5$ | . . . . |
| Glass | $2{\cdot}60 \times 10^3$ | 1400 | . . . . | $6{\cdot}70 \times 10^2$ | . . . . | . . . . |
| Ice | $9{\cdot}20 \times 10^2$ | 273 | . . . . | $2{\cdot}10 \times 10^3$ | $3{\cdot}34 \times 10^5$ | . . . . |
| Glycerol | $1{\cdot}26 \times 10^3$ | 291 | 563 | $2{\cdot}43 \times 10^3$ | $1{\cdot}81 \times 10^5$ | $8{\cdot}30 \times 10^5$ |
| Methanol | $7{\cdot}91 \times 10^2$ | 175 | 338 | $2{\cdot}52 \times 10^3$ | $9{\cdot}9 \times 10^4$ | $1{\cdot}12 \times 10^6$ |
| Sea Water | $1{\cdot}02 \times 10^3$ | 264 | 377 | $3{\cdot}93 \times 10^3$ | . . . . | . . . . |
| Water | $1{\cdot}00 \times 10^3$ | 273 | 373 | $4{\cdot}18 \times 10^3$ | $3{\cdot}34 \times 10^5$ | $2{\cdot}26 \times 10^6$ |
| Air | 1·29 | . . . . | . . . . | | . . . . | |
| Hydrogen | $9{\cdot}0 \times 10^{-2}$ | 14 | 20 | $1{\cdot}43 \times 10^4$ | . . . . | $4{\cdot}50 \times 10^5$ |
| Nitrogen | 1·25 | 63 | 77 | $1{\cdot}04 \times 10^3$ | . . . . | $2{\cdot}00 \times 10^5$ |
| Oxygen | 1·43 | 55 | 90 | $9{\cdot}18 \times 10^2$ | . . . . | $2{\cdot}40 \times 10^4$ |

The gas densities refer to a temperature of 273 K and a pressure of $1{\cdot}01 \times 10^5$ Pa.

*Page two*

MARKS | DO NOT WRITE IN THIS MARGIN

**Total marks — 140 marks**

**Attempt ALL questions**

1.  An athlete competes in a one hundred metre race on a flat track, as shown in Figure 1A.

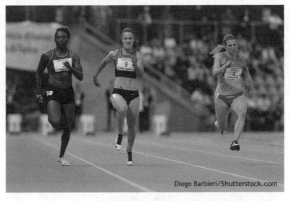

Diego Barbieri/Shutterstock.com

Figure 1A

Starting from rest, the athlete's speed for the first 3·10 seconds of the race can be modelled using the relationship

$$v = 0 \cdot 4t^2 + 2t$$

where the symbols have their usual meaning.

According to this model:

(a) determine the speed of the athlete at $t = 3 \cdot 10 \, \text{s}$;    **2**

*Space for working and answer*

(b) determine, using **calculus** methods, the distance travelled by the athlete in this time.    **3**

*Space for working and answer*

MARKS | DO NOT WRITE IN THIS MARGIN

2. (a) As part of a lesson, a teacher swings a sphere tied to a light string as shown in Figure 2A. The path of the sphere is a vertical circle as shown in Figure 2B.

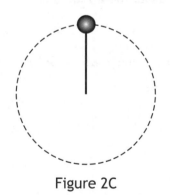

Figure 2A            Figure 2B

(i) On Figure 2C, show the forces acting on the sphere as it passes through its highest point.

You must name these forces and show their directions.          **1**

Figure 2C

MARKS | DO NOT WRITE IN THIS MARGIN

**2. (a) (continued)**

(ii) On Figure 2D, show the forces acting on the sphere as it passes through its lowest point.

You must name these forces and show their directions. **1**

Figure 2D

(iii) The sphere of mass 0·35 kg can be considered to be moving at a constant speed.

The centripetal force acting on the sphere is 4·0 N.

Determine the magnitude of the tension in the light string when the sphere is at:

(A) the highest position in its circular path; **2**

*Space for working and answer*

(B) the lowest position in its circular path. **1**

*Space for working and answer*

MARKS | DO NOT WRITE IN THIS MARGIN

**2.    (continued)**

(b)  The speed of the sphere is now gradually reduced until the sphere no longer travels in a circular path.

Explain why the sphere no longer travels in a circular path.        **2**

(c)  The teacher again swings the sphere with constant speed in a vertical circle. The student shown in Figure 2E observes the sphere moving up and down vertically with simple harmonic motion.

The period of this motion is 1·4 s.

Figure 2E

Figure 2F represents the path of the sphere as observed by the student.

Figure 2F

2. **(c) (continued)**

On Figure 2G, sketch a graph showing how the vertical displacement $s$ of the sphere from its central position varies with time $t$, as it moves from its highest position to its lowest position.

Numerical values are required on both axes.

**3**

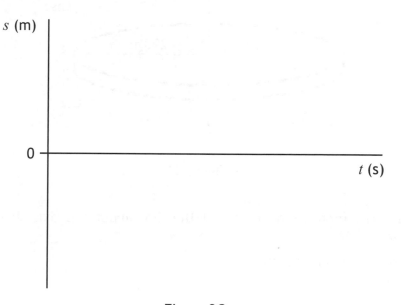

Figure 2G

(An additional diagram, if required, can be found on *Page forty-two*.)

**[Turn over**

MARKS | DO NOT WRITE IN THIS MARGIN

3. A student uses a solid, uniform circular disc of radius 290 mm and mass 0·40 kg as part of an investigation into rotational motion.

The disc is shown in Figure 3A.

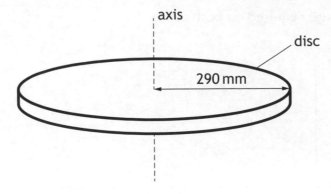

Figure 3A

(a) Calculate the moment of inertia of the disc about the axis shown in Figure 3A.

*Space for working and answer*

**3**

MARKS | DO NOT WRITE IN THIS MARGIN

**3. (continued)**

(b) The disc is now mounted horizontally on the axle of a rotational motion sensor as shown in Figure 3B.

The axle is on a frictionless bearing. A thin cord is wound around a stationary pulley which is attached to the axle.

The moment of inertia of the pulley and axle can be considered negligible.

The pulley has a radius of 7·5 mm and a force of 8·0 N is applied to the free end of the cord.

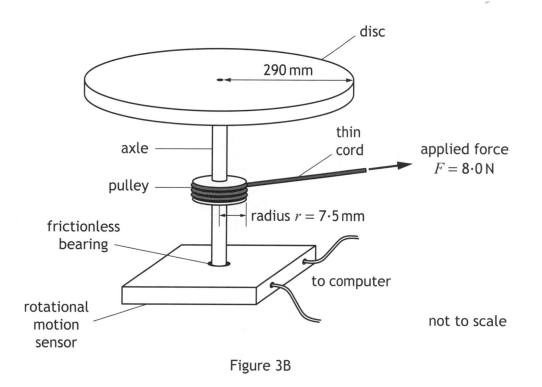

Figure 3B

(i) Calculate the torque applied to the pulley.

*Space for working and answer*

3

(ii) Calculate the angular acceleration produced by this torque.

*Space for working and answer*

3

MARKS | DO NOT WRITE IN THIS MARGIN

3.  (b)  (continued)

(iii)  The cord becomes detached from the pulley after 0·25 m has unwound.

By considering the angular displacement of the disc, determine its angular velocity when the cord becomes detached.

*Space for working and answer*

**5**

MARKS | DO NOT WRITE IN THIS MARGIN

3.  **(continued)**

(c)  In a second experiment the disc has an angular velocity of 12 rad s$^{-1}$.

The student now drops a small 25 g cube vertically onto the disc. The cube sticks to the disc.

The centre of mass of the cube is 220 mm from the axis of rotation, as shown in Figure 3C.

Figure 3C

Calculate the angular velocity of the system immediately after the cube was dropped onto the disc.

*Space for working and answer*

5

4. The NASA space probe Dawn has travelled to and orbited large asteroids in the solar system. Dawn has a mass of 1240 kg.

The table gives information about two large asteroids orbited by Dawn. Both asteroids can be considered to be spherical and remote from other large objects.

| Name | Mass ($\times 10^{20}$ kg) | Radius (km) |
|---|---|---|
| Vesta | 2·59 | 263 |
| Ceres | 9·39 | 473 |

(a) Dawn began orbiting Vesta, in a circular orbit, at a height of 680 km above the surface of the asteroid. The gravitational force acting on Dawn at this altitude was 24·1 N.

    (i) Show that the tangential velocity of Dawn in this orbit is 135 m s$^{-1}$.    **2**

    *Space for working and answer*

    (ii) Calculate the orbital period of Dawn.    **3**

    *Space for working and answer*

MARKS | DO NOT WRITE IN THIS MARGIN

4.　(continued)

(b)　Later in its mission, Dawn entered orbit around Ceres. It then moved from a high orbit to a lower orbit around the asteroid.

(i)　State what is meant by the *gravitational potential of a point in space*.　**1**

(ii)　Dawn has a gravitational potential of $-1\cdot29 \times 10^4\,\mathrm{J\,kg^{-1}}$ in the high orbit and a gravitational potential of $-3\cdot22 \times 10^4\,\mathrm{J\,kg^{-1}}$ in the lower orbit.

Determine the change in the potential energy of Dawn as a result of this change in orbit.　**4**

*Space for working and answer*

MARKS | DO NOT WRITE IN THIS MARGIN

5. Two students are discussing objects escaping from the gravitational pull of the Earth. They make the following statements:

Student 1: A rocket has to accelerate until it reaches the escape velocity of the Earth in order to escape its gravitational pull.

Student 2: The moon is travelling slower than the escape velocity of the Earth and yet it has escaped.

Use your knowledge of physics to comment on these statements. **3**

[Turn over for next question

**DO NOT WRITE ON THIS PAGE**

**6.** A Hertzsprung-Russell (H-R) diagram is shown in Figure 6A.

Figure 6A

(a) All stars on the main sequence release energy by converting hydrogen to helium. This process is known as the proton-proton (p-p) chain. One stage in the p-p chain is shown.

$$^1_1H + ^1_1H \rightarrow ^2_1H + x + y$$

Name particles $x$ and $y$.

2

(b) The luminosity of the Sun is $3{\cdot}9 \times 10^{26}$ W. The star Procyon B has a luminosity of $4{\cdot}9 \times 10^{-4}$ solar units and a radius of $1{\cdot}2 \times 10^{-2}$ solar radii.

(i) On the H-R diagram, circle the star at the position of Procyon B.

(An additional diagram, if required, can be found on *Page forty-two*.)

1

(ii) What type of star is Procyon B?

1

MARKS | DO NOT WRITE IN THIS MARGIN

**6.    (b)    (continued)**

   (iii)  The apparent brightness of Procyon B when viewed from Earth is $1 \cdot 3 \times 10^{-12} \, \mathrm{W \, m^{-2}}$.

   Calculate the distance of Procyon B from Earth.                4

   *Space for working and answer*

   (c)  The expression

$$\frac{L}{L_0} = 1 \cdot 5 \left( \frac{M}{M_0} \right)^{3 \cdot 5}$$

can be used to approximate the relationship between a star's mass $M$ and its luminosity $L$.

$L_0$ is the luminosity of the Sun (1 solar unit) and $M_0$ is the mass of the Sun.

This expression is valid for stars of mass between $2M_0$ and $20M_0$.

Spica is a star which has mass $10 \cdot 3 M_0$.

Determine the approximate luminosity of Spica in solar units.                2

*Space for working and answer*

MARKS | DO NOT WRITE IN THIS MARGIN

**7.** Laser light is often described as having a single frequency. However, in practice a laser will emit photons with a range of frequencies.

Quantum physics links the frequency of a photon to its energy.

Therefore the photons emitted by a laser have a range of energies ($\Delta E$). The range of photon energies is related to the lifetime ($\Delta t$) of the atom in the excited state.

A graph showing the variation of intensity with frequency for light from two types of laser is shown in Figure 7A.

Figure 7A

(a) By considering the Heisenberg uncertainty principle, state how the lifetime of atoms in the excited state in the neodymium:YAG laser compares with the lifetime of atoms in the excited state in the argon ion laser.

Justify your answer.

2

MARKS | DO NOT WRITE IN THIS MARGIN

7. **(continued)**

(b) In another type of laser, an atom is in the excited state for a time of $5 \cdot 0 \times 10^{-6}$ s.

    (i) Calculate the minimum uncertainty in the energy ($\Delta E_{min}$) of a photon emitted when the atom returns to its unexcited state.    **3**

    *Space for working and answer*

    (ii) Determine a value for the range of frequencies ($\Delta f$) of the photons emitted by this laser.    **3**

    *Space for working and answer*

8.  A student is investigating simple harmonic motion. An oscillating mass on a spring, and a motion sensor connected to a computer, are used in the investigation. This is shown in Figure 8A.

not to scale

oscillating mass on a spring

motion sensor

Figure 8A

The student raises the mass from its rest position and then releases it. The computer starts recording data when the mass is released.

(a)  The student plans to model the displacement $y$ of the mass from its rest position, using the expression

$$y = A\sin \omega t$$

where the symbols have their usual meaning.

Explain why the student is incorrect.

1

8. **(continued)**

(b) (i) The unbalanced force acting on the mass is given by the expression

$$F = -m\omega^2 y$$

Hooke's Law is given by the expression

$$F = -k y$$

where $k$ is the spring constant.

By comparing these expressions, show that the frequency of the oscillation can be described by the relationship

$$f = \frac{1}{2\pi}\sqrt{\frac{k}{m}}$$

**2**

(ii) The student measures the mass to be 0·50 kg and the period of oscillation to be 0·80 s.

Determine a value for the spring constant $k$.

**3**

*Space for working and answer*

MARKS | DO NOT WRITE IN THIS MARGIN

8. **(b)** **(continued)**

(iii) The student plans to repeat the experiment using the same mass and a second spring, which has a spring constant twice the value of the original.

Determine the expected period of oscillation of the mass.

2

(c) The student obtains graphs showing the variation of displacement with time, velocity with time and acceleration with time.

The student forgets to label the y-axis for each graph.

Complete the labelling of the y-axis of each graph in Figure 8B.

2

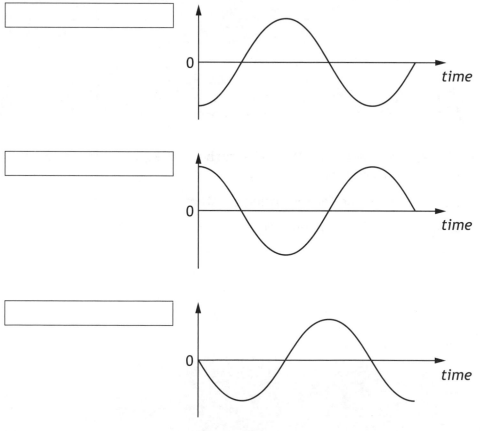

Figure 8B

MARKS | DO NOT WRITE IN THIS MARGIN

9. A wave travelling along a string is represented by the relationship

$$y = 9 \cdot 50 \times 10^{-4} \sin(922t - 4 \cdot 50x)$$

(a) (i) Show that the frequency of the wave is 147 Hz.   **1**

*Space for working and answer*

(ii) Determine the speed of the wave.   **4**

*Space for working and answer*

(iii) The wave loses energy as it travels along the string.

At one point, the energy of the wave has decreased to one eighth of its original value.

Calculate the amplitude of the wave at this point.   **3**

*Space for working and answer*

**[Turn over**

MARKS | DO NOT WRITE IN THIS MARGIN

9.  (continued)

(b)  The speed of a wave on a string can also be described by the relationship

$$v = \sqrt{\frac{T}{\mu}}$$

where $v$ is the speed of the wave,

$T$ is the tension in the string, and

$\mu$ is the mass per unit length of the string.

A string of length 0·69 m has a mass of $9.0 \times 10^{-3}$ kg.

A wave is travelling along the string with a speed of 203 m s$^{-1}$.

Calculate the tension in the string.    **3**

*Space for working and answer*

MARKS | DO NOT WRITE IN THIS MARGIN

**9. (continued)**

(c) When a string is fixed at both ends and plucked, a stationary wave is produced.

    (i) Explain briefly, in terms of the superposition of waves, how the stationary wave is produced.

                                                       1

    (ii) The string is vibrating at its fundamental frequency of 270 Hz and produces the stationary wave pattern shown in Figure 9A.

Figure 9A

Figure 9B shows the same string vibrating at a frequency called its third harmonic.

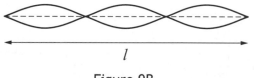

Figure 9B

Determine the frequency of the third harmonic.　　　　　　　1

[BLANK PAGE]

DO NOT WRITE ON THIS PAGE

MARKS | DO NOT WRITE IN THIS MARGIN

10. The internal structure of some car windscreens produces an effect which can be likened to that obtained by slits in a grating.

A passenger in a car observes a distant red traffic light and notices that the red light is surrounded by a pattern of bright spots.

This is shown in Figure 10A.

Figure 10A

(a) Explain how the **two-dimensional** pattern of bright spots shown in Figure 10A is produced.

2

(b) The traffic light changes to green. Apart from colour, state a difference that would be observed in the pattern of bright spots.

Justify your answer.

2

**10.  (continued)**

(c)  An LED from the traffic light is tested to determine the wavelength by shining its light through a set of Young's double slits, as shown in Figure 10B.

The fringe separation is $(13\cdot0 \pm 0\cdot5)$ mm and the double slit separation is $(0\cdot41 \pm 0\cdot01)$ mm.

Figure 10B

(i)  Calculate the wavelength of the light from the LED.    **3**

*Space for working and answer*

**10. (c) (continued)**

    (ii)   Determine the absolute uncertainty in this wavelength.     **5**

       *Space for working and answer*

    (iii)   The experiment is now repeated with the screen moved further away from the slits.

       Explain why this is the most effective way of reducing the uncertainty in the calculated value of the wavelength.     **1**

MARKS | DO NOT WRITE IN THIS MARGIN

11. (a) State what is meant by the term *electric field strength*. **1**

(b) A, B, C and D are the vertices of a square of side 0·12 m.

Two +4·0 nC point charges are placed at positions B and D as shown in Figure 11A.

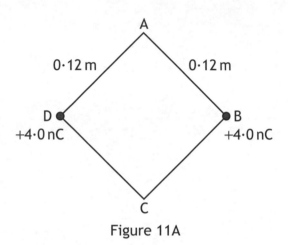

Figure 11A

(i) Show that the magnitude of the electric field strength at position A is $3·5 \times 10^3 \, \text{N C}^{-1}$. **3**

*Space for working and answer*

MARKS | DO NOT WRITE IN THIS MARGIN

11.  (b)  (continued)

   (ii)  A +1·9 nC point charge is placed at position A.

   Calculate the magnitude of the force acting on this charge.    3

   *Space for working and answer*

   (iii)  State the direction of the force acting on this charge.    1

   (iv)  A fourth point charge is now placed at position C so that the resultant force on the charge at position A is zero.

   Determine the magnitude of the charge placed at position C.    4

   *Space for working and answer*

12. A velocity selector is used as the initial part of a larger apparatus that is designed to measure properties of ions of different elements.

The velocity selector has a region in which there is a uniform electric field and a uniform magnetic field. These fields are perpendicular to each other and also perpendicular to the initial velocity $v$ of the ions.

This is shown in Figure 12A.

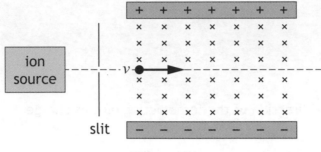

Figure 12A

A beam of chlorine ions consists of a number of isotopes including $^{35}Cl^+$.

The magnitude of the charge on a $^{35}Cl^+$ ion is $1\cdot60 \times 10^{-19}$ C.

The magnitude of electric force on a $^{35}Cl^+$ chlorine ion is $4\cdot00 \times 10^{-15}$ N.

The ions enter the apparatus with a range of speeds.

The magnetic induction is 115 mT.

(a) State the direction of the magnetic force on a $^{35}Cl^+$ ion.　　1

(b) By considering the electric and magnetic forces acting on a $^{35}Cl^+$ ion, determine the speed of the $^{35}Cl^+$ ions that will pass through the apparatus without being deflected.　　3

*Space for working and answer*

MARKS | DO NOT WRITE IN THIS MARGIN

**12. (continued)**

(c) $^{35}Cl^+$ ions that are travelling at a velocity less than that determined in (b) are observed to follow the path shown in Figure 12B.

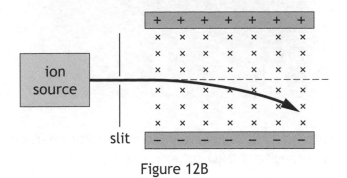

Figure 12B

Explain, in terms of their velocity, why these ions follow this path.    **2**

(d) $^{37}Cl^{2+}$ ions are also present in the beam. $^{37}Cl^{2+}$ ions have a greater mass and a greater charge than $^{35}Cl^+$ ions. Some $^{37}Cl^{2+}$ ions also pass through the apparatus without being deflected.

State the speed of these ions.

You must justify your answer.    **2**

   **[Turn over**

MARKS | DO NOT WRITE IN THIS MARGIN

13. A student purchases a capacitor with capacitance 1·0 F. The capacitor, which has negligible resistance, is used to supply short bursts of energy to the audio system in a car when there is high energy demand on the car battery.

The instructions state that the capacitor must be fully charged from the 12 V d.c. car battery through a 1·0 kΩ series resistor.

(a) Show that the time constant for this charging circuit is $1\cdot0 \times 10^3$ s.

*Space for working and answer*

2

MARKS | DO NOT WRITE IN THIS MARGIN

**13.** **(continued)**

(b) The student carries out an experiment to monitor the voltage across the capacitor while it is being charged.

(i) Draw a diagram of the circuit which would enable the student to carry out this experiment.

1

(ii) The student draws the graph shown in Figure 13A.

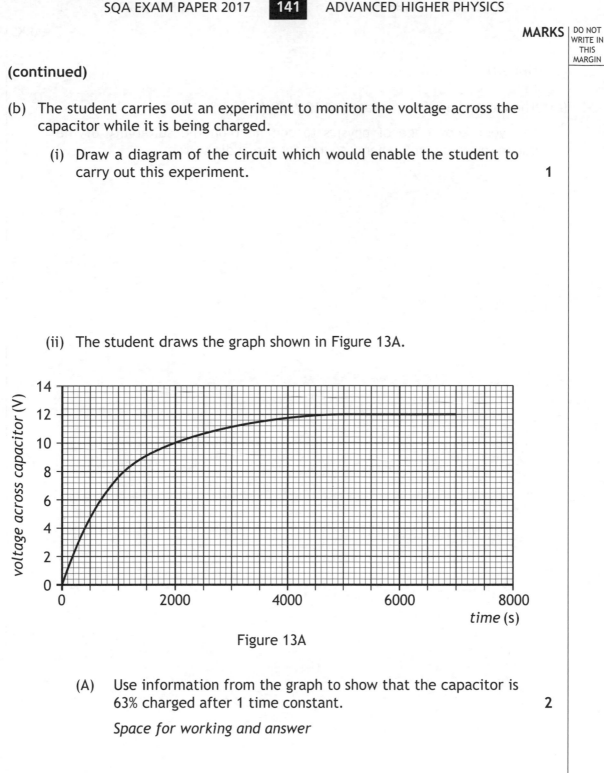

Figure 13A

(A) Use information from the graph to show that the capacitor is 63% charged after 1 time constant.

*Space for working and answer*

2

(B) Use information from the graph to determine how many time constants are required for this capacitor to be considered fully charged.

1

[**Turn over**

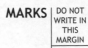

MARKS | DO NOT WRITE IN THIS MARGIN

13.   (continued)

(c)   The car audio system is rated at 12 V, 20 W.

Use your knowledge of physics to comment on the suitability of the capacitor as the only energy source for the audio system.    **3**

[Turn over for next question

**DO NOT WRITE ON THIS PAGE**

**14.** A student designs a loudspeaker circuit.

A capacitor and an inductor are used in the circuit so that high frequency signals are passed to a small "tweeter" loudspeaker and low frequency signals are passed to a large "woofer" loudspeaker.

Each loudspeaker has a resistance of $8 \cdot 0\,\Omega$.

The circuit diagram is shown in Figure 14A.

Figure 14A

The circuit is designed to have a "crossover" frequency of $3 \cdot 0\,\text{kHz}$: at frequencies above $3 \cdot 0\,\text{kHz}$ there is a greater current in the tweeter and at frequencies below $3 \cdot 0\,\text{kHz}$ there is a greater current in the woofer.

(a) Explain how the use of a capacitor and an inductor allows:

(i)  high frequency signals to be passed to the tweeter;     **1**

(ii) low frequency signals to be passed to the woofer.     **1**

MARKS | DO NOT WRITE IN THIS MARGIN

14.    (continued)

(b)    At the crossover frequency, both the reactance of the capacitor and the reactance of the inductor are equal to the resistance of each loudspeaker.

Calculate the inductance required to provide an inductive reactance of $8 \cdot 0 \, \Omega$ when the frequency of the signal is $3 \cdot 0 \, \text{kHz}$.

3

*Space for working and answer*

14.  (continued)

(c)  In a box of components, the student finds an inductor and decides to determine its inductance. The student constructs the circuit shown in Figure 14B.

Figure 14B

The student obtains data from the experiment and presents the data on the graph shown in Figure 14C.

Figure 14C

MARKS | DO NOT WRITE IN THIS MARGIN

**14. (c) (continued)**

(i) Determine the inductance of the inductor.    **4**

*Space for working and answer*

(ii) The student was advised to include a diode in the circuit to prevent damage to the laptop when the switch is opened.

Explain why this is necessary.    **1**

**[END OF QUESTION PAPER]**

## ADDITIONAL SPACE FOR ANSWERS AND ROUGH WORK

Additional diagram for question 2 (c)

Figure 2G

Additional diagram for question 6 (b) (i)

Figure 6A

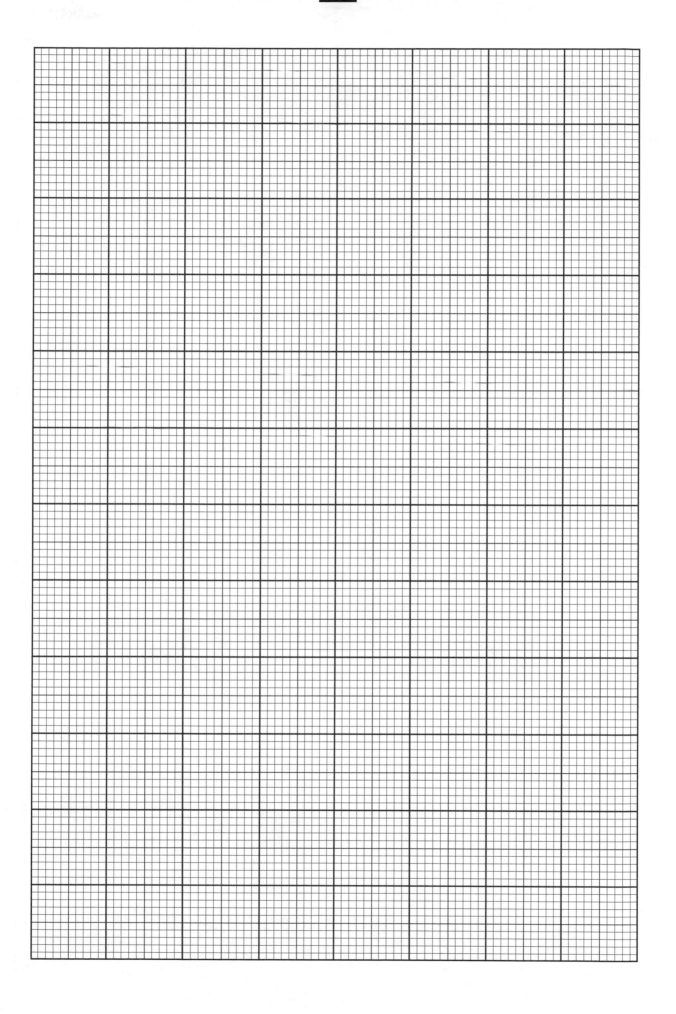

**ADDITIONAL SPACE FOR ANSWERS AND ROUGH WORK**

MARKS | DO NOT WRITE IN THIS MARGIN

**ADDITIONAL SPACE FOR ANSWERS AND ROUGH WORK**

ADDITIONAL SPACE FOR ANSWERS AND ROUGH WORK

MARKS

DO NOT WRITE IN THIS MARGIN

ADVANCED HIGHER

# Answers

# SQA ADVANCED HIGHER PHYSICS 2017

## ADVANCED HIGHER PHYSICS
## 2015 SPECIMEN QUESTION PAPER

| Question | | | Expected response | | Max mark | Additional guidance |
|---|---|---|---|---|---|---|
| 1. | (a) | | $\omega = \dfrac{\theta}{t}$ $\qquad$ (1) <br><br> $= \dfrac{1250 \times 2 \times \pi}{60}$ $\qquad$ (1) <br><br> $= 131\ \text{rad s}^{-1}$ | | 2 | If final answer is not shown then maximum of 1 mark can be awarded. |
| | (b) | (i) | $\alpha = \dfrac{\omega_1 - \omega_0}{t}$ $\qquad$ (1) <br><br> $= \dfrac{131 - 7 \cdot 50}{12}$ $\qquad$ (1) <br><br> $= 10 \cdot 3\ \text{rad s}^{-2}$ $\qquad$ (1) | | 3 | Accept: <br> 10 <br> 10·3 <br> 10·29 <br> 10·292 |
| | | (ii) | $\theta = \omega_0 t + \dfrac{1}{2}\alpha t^2$ $\qquad$ (1) <br><br> $= 7 \cdot 50 \times 12 \cdot 0 + 0 \cdot 5 \times 10 \cdot 3 \times 12 \cdot 0^2$ $\qquad$ (1) <br><br> $= 831 \cdot 6\ \text{(rad)}$ $\qquad$ (1) <br><br> $\text{revolutions} = \dfrac{831 \cdot 6}{2\pi}$ $\qquad$ (1) <br><br> $= 132$ $\qquad$ (1) | | 5 | If candidate stops here unit must be present for mark 3. <br> Accept: <br> 130 <br> 132 <br> 132·4 <br> 132·35 |
| | (c) | | $\text{centripetal force} = m\omega^2 r$ $\qquad$ (1) <br><br> $= 1 \cdot 5 \times 10^{-2} \times 131^2 \times 0 \cdot 28$ $\qquad$ (1) <br><br> $= 72\ \text{N}$ $\qquad$ (1) | | 3 | Accept: <br> 70 <br> 72 <br> 72·1 <br> 72·08 |
| | (d) | (i) | The drum exerts a centripetal/central force on the clothing. $\qquad$ (1) <br><br> No centripetal/central force acting on water. $\qquad$ (1) | | 2 | |
| | | (ii) | $\qquad$ (1) | | 1 | |
| | | (iii) | Centripetal force decreases ... $\qquad$ (1) <br> as mass of wet clothing decreases $\qquad$ (1) | | 2 | |
| 2. | (a) | | $I = \dfrac{1}{2}mr^2$ $\qquad$ (1) <br><br> $= 0 \cdot 5 \times 6 \cdot 0 \times 0 \cdot 50^2$ $\qquad$ (1) <br><br> $= 0 \cdot 75\ \text{kg m}^2$ | | 2 | If final answer is not shown then maximum of 1 mark can be awarded. |

| Question | | | Expected response | | Max mark | Additional guidance |
|---|---|---|---|---|---|---|
| | (b) | (i) | 2 kg mass:<br>$\quad I = mr^2$ **(1)**<br>$\quad\quad = 2\cdot0\times0\cdot40^2$ **(1)**<br>$\quad\quad = 0\cdot32\ (\text{kg m}^2)$<br>Total $= 0\cdot32 + 0\cdot75 = 1\cdot1\ \text{kg m}^2$ **(1)** | | 3 | Accept:<br>1<br>$1\cdot1$<br>$1\cdot07$<br>$1\cdot070$ |
| | | (ii) | $\quad I_1\omega_1 = I_2\omega_2$ **(1)**<br>$0\cdot75\times12 = 1\cdot1\times\omega_2$ **(1)**<br>$\quad\quad \omega_2 = 8\cdot2\ \text{rad s}^{-1}$ **(1)** | | 3 | Accept:<br>8<br>$8\cdot2$<br>$8\cdot18$<br>$8\cdot182$<br>Also accept $8\cdot4$ if $1\cdot07$ is clearly used. |
| | | (iii) | No external torque acts on system.<br>**Or**, 2 kg can be considered as a point mass. | | 1 | |
| | (c) | | • the (final) angular velocity will be greater **(1)**<br>• the final moment of inertia is less than in b(ii) **(1)** | | 2 | Reference must be made to moment of inertia for the second mark. Insufficient to say "sphere rolls off" without effect on moment of inertia. |
| 3. | (a) | (i) | $\dfrac{GM_E m}{r^2} = m\omega^2 r$<br><br>$\omega = \dfrac{2\pi}{T}$ **(1)**<br><br>$\dfrac{GM_E m}{r^2} = m\dfrac{4\pi^2}{T^2}r$ **(1)**<br><br>$T = 2\pi\sqrt{\dfrac{r^3}{GM_g}}$ | | 2 | To access any marks candidates must start with equating the forces/acceleration.<br><br>A maximum of 1 mark if final equation is not shown. |
| | | (ii) | $T = 2\pi\sqrt{\dfrac{(6\cdot4\times10^6 + 4\cdot0\times10^5)^3}{6\cdot67\times10^{-11}\times6\cdot0\times10^{24}}}$ **(1)**<br><br>$\quad = 5\cdot6\times10^3\ \text{s}$ **(1)** | | 2 | Accept:<br>6<br>$5\cdot6$<br>$5\cdot57$<br>$5\cdot569$ |
| | (b) | (i) | Value from graph $4\cdot15\times10^5$ (m) **(1)**<br><br>$mg = \dfrac{GM_E m}{r^2}$ **(1)**<br><br>$g = \dfrac{GM_E}{r^2}$ **(1)**<br><br>$\quad = \dfrac{6\cdot67\times10^{-11}\times6\cdot0\times10^{24}}{(4\cdot15\times10^5 + 6\cdot4\times10^6)^2}$<br><br>$\quad = 8\cdot6\ \text{N kg}^{-1}$ **(1)** | | 4 | Accept:<br>9<br>$8\cdot6$<br>$8\cdot62$<br>$8\cdot617$ |
| | | (ii) | Less atmospheric drag/friction **or** will reduce running costs. **(1)** | | 1 | |

| Question | | | Expected response | Max mark | Additional guidance |
|---|---|---|---|---|---|
| | (c) | | The gravitational field is smaller at the ISS (compared to Earth). (1) <br><br> The clocks on ISS will run faster (than those on Earth). (1) | 2 | |
| 4. | (a) | | Betelgeuse will look red-orange. | 1 | |
| | (b) | (i)(A) | $L = 4\pi r^2 \sigma T^4$ (1) <br> $L = 4 \times \pi \times (5 \cdot 49 \times 10^{10})^2 \times 5 \cdot 67 \times 10^{-8}$ <br> $\times (1 \cdot 20 \times 10^4)^4$ (1) <br> $L = 4 \cdot 45 \times 10^{31}\,\text{W}$ (1) | 3 | Accept: <br> $4 \cdot 5 \times 10^{31}$ <br> $4 \cdot 45 \times 10^{31}$ <br> $4 \cdot 453 \times 10^{31}$ <br> $4 \cdot 4531 \times 10^{31}$ |
| | | (i)(B) | Rigel/stars behave as black body(ies). | 1 | |
| | | (ii) | $\%\Delta r = \dfrac{0 \cdot 50}{5 \cdot 49} \times 100\% = 9 \cdot 1\%$ (1) <br><br> $\%\Delta T = \dfrac{0 \cdot 05}{1 \cdot 20} \times 100\% = 4 \cdot 2\%$ (1) <br><br> Total $\%\Delta = \sqrt{(9 \cdot 1 \times 2)^2 + (4 \cdot 2 \times 4)^2}$ (1) <br> $= 25\%$ <br> $\Delta L = 4 \cdot 45 \times 10^{31} \times 0 \cdot 25 = 1 \times 10^{31}\,\text{W}$ (1) | 4 | Accept: <br> $1 \cdot 1$ <br> $1 \cdot 11$ |
| | (c) | | $b = \dfrac{L}{4\pi r^2}$ (1) <br><br> $= \dfrac{4 \cdot 45 \times 10^{31}}{4 \times \pi \times (773 \times 365 \times 24 \times 60 \times 60 \times 3 \cdot 00 \times 10^8)^2}$ (1) <br> For ly to m conversion (1) <br> $= 6 \cdot 62 \times 10^{-8}\,\text{Wm}^{-2}$ (1) | 4 | Accept: <br> $6 \cdot 6 \times 10^{-8}$ <br> $6 \cdot 62 \times 10^{-8}$ <br> $6 \cdot 621 \times 10^{-8}$ <br> $6 \cdot 6212 \times 10^{-8}$ <br> The use of $3 \cdot 14$ or $365 \cdot 25$ may give $6 \cdot 61$. |
| | (d) | | Any two from: <br> • (Most) hydrogen fusion has stopped. <br> • Radius has (significantly) increased. <br> • Surface temperature has decreased. <br> • Core gets hotter. | 2 | |
| 5. | (a) | (i) | Acceleration is proportional to displacement (from a fixed point) and is always directed to (that) fixed point. <br> **OR** <br> The unbalanced force is proportional to the displacement (from a fixed point) and is always directed to (that) fixed point. | 1 | Accept: <br> $F = -kx$ <br> or <br> $a = -kx$ |
| | | (ii) | From graph $T = 5 \cdot 0$ (s) (1) <br> $\rightarrow f = \dfrac{1}{T} = \dfrac{1}{5 \cdot 0} = 0 \cdot 20\,\text{s}$ <br> $\omega = 2\pi f$ (1) <br> $= 2 \times \pi \times 0 \cdot 20$ (1) <br> $= 1 \cdot 3\,\text{rads}^{-1}$ (1) | 4 | Accept: <br> $1$ <br> $1 \cdot 3$ <br> $1 \cdot 26$ <br> $1 \cdot 257$ <br> Use of $\omega = \dfrac{2\pi}{T}$ is possible. |
| | | (iii) | $a = (-)\omega^2 y$ (1) <br> $a = (-)1 \cdot 3^2 \times (-)4 \cdot 0$ (1) <br> $a = (-)6 \cdot 8\,\text{ms}^{-2}$ (1) | 3 | Accept: <br> $7$ <br> $6 \cdot 8$ <br> $6 \cdot 76$ <br> $6 \cdot 760$ |

| Question | | | Expected response | Max mark | Additional guidance |
|---|---|---|---|---|---|
| | | (iv) | Sine shape graph for one period of oscillation from $t = 0\,s$ to $t = 5\,s$ $\hspace{2cm}$ (1) $v_{max} = \pm\omega\sqrt{(A^2 - y^2)}$ $\hspace{2cm}$ (1) $v_{max} = \pm1\cdot3\times\sqrt{(4\cdot0^2 - 0^2)}$ $v_{max} = \pm5\cdot2\,m\,s^{-1}$ $\hspace{2cm}$ (1) | 3 | Award a maximum of 2 marks if the labels, units or origin is/are missing. |
| | | (v) | $E_p = \dfrac{1}{2}m\omega^2 y^2$ $\hspace{1cm}$ (1) $E_p = 0\cdot5\times85\times1\cdot3^2\times4\cdot0^2$ $\hspace{0.3cm}$ (1) $E_p = 1\cdot1\times10^3\,J$ $\hspace{1.5cm}$ (1) | 3 | Accept: $1\times10^3$ $1\cdot1\times10^3$ $1\cdot15\times10^3$ $1\cdot149\times10^3$ |

| Question | | | Expected response | Additional guidance |
|---|---|---|---|---|
| | (b) | | The whole candidate response should first be read to establish its overall quality in terms of accuracy and relevance to the problem/situation presented. There may be strengths and weaknesses in the candidate response: assessors should focus as far as possible on the strengths, taking account of weaknesses (errors or omissions) only where they detract from the overall answer in a significant way, which should then be taken into account when determining whether the response demonstrates reasonable, limited or no understanding. Assessors should use their professional judgement to apply the guidance below to the wide range of possible candidate responses. | This open-ended question requires comment on possible reasons for discrepancies in assuming the SHM model. Candidate responses may include one or more of: snowboarder going too far; not a semicircle; movement down the half pipe; additional force caused by snowboarder or other relevant ideas/concepts. |
| | | | **3 marks:** The candidate has demonstrated a **good** conceptual understanding of the physics involved, providing a logically correct response to the problem/situation presented. This type of response might include a statement of principle(s) involved, a relationship or equation, and the application of these to respond to the problem/situation. This does not mean the answer has to be what might be termed an "excellent" answer or a "complete" one. | In response to this question, a **good** understanding might be demonstrated by a candidate response that: • makes a judgement on suitability based on one relevant physics idea/concept, in a **detailed/developed** response that is **correct or largely correct** (any weaknesses are minor and do not detract from the overall response), **OR** • makes judgement(s) on suitability based on a range of relevant physics ideas/concepts, in a response that is **correct or largely correct** (any weaknesses are minor and do not detract from the overall response), **OR** • otherwise demonstrates a good understanding of the physics involved. |

| Question | Expected response | Additional guidance |
|---|---|---|
| | **2 marks:** The candidate has demonstrated a **reasonable** understanding of the physics involved, showing that the problem/situation is understood.<br><br>This type of response might make some statement(s) that is/are relevant to the problem/situation, for example, a statement of relevant principle(s) or identification of a relevant relationship or equation. | In response to this question, a **reasonable** understanding might be demonstrated by a candidate response that:'<br>• makes a judgement on suitability based on one or more relevant physics idea(s)/concept(s), in a response that is **largely correct** but has **weaknesses** which detract to a small extent from the overall response, **OR**<br>• otherwise demonstrates a reasonable understanding of the physics involved. |
| | **1 mark:** The candidate has demonstrated a **limited** understanding of the physics involved, showing that a little of the physics that is relevant to the problem/situation is understood.<br><br>The candidate has made some statement(s) that is/are relevant to the problem/situation. | In response to this question, a **limited** understanding might be demonstrated by a candidate response that:<br>• makes a judgement on suitability based on one or more relevant physics idea(s)/concept(s), in a response that has **weaknesses** which detract to a large extent from the overall response, **OR**<br>• otherwise demonstrates a limited understanding of the physics involved. |
| | **0 marks:** The candidate has demonstrated **no** understanding of the physics that is relevant to the problem/situation.<br><br>The candidate has made no statement(s) that is/are relevant to the problem/situation. | Where the candidate has *only* demonstrated knowledge and understanding of physics **that is not relevant to the problem/situation presented,** 0 marks should be awarded. |

| Question | | | Expected response | Max mark | Additional guidance |
|---|---|---|---|---|---|
| 6. | (a) | | Electrostatic force between the nucleus/proton and the electron.  (1) | 1 | Any other forces shown 0 marks. |
| | (b) | (i) | (Electrostatic force = centripetal force)<br>$$\frac{Q_1Q_2}{4\pi\varepsilon_0 r^2} = \frac{mv^2}{r}$$ (1)<br>$$\frac{e^2}{4\pi\varepsilon_0 r^2} = \frac{mv^2}{r}$$<br>$$mv^2 = \frac{e^2}{4\pi\varepsilon_0 r}$$<br>$$\frac{1}{2}mv^2 = \frac{e^2}{8\pi\varepsilon_0 r}$$ (1)<br>$$E_k = \frac{e^2}{8\pi\varepsilon_0 r}$$ | 2 | Equations must be shown from Relationships Sheet to gain any marks.<br><br>If final line is not shown then maximum of 1 mark only can be awarded. |

| Question | | | Expected response | Max mark | Additional guidance |
|---|---|---|---|---|---|
| | | (ii) | $E_k = \dfrac{e^2}{8\pi\varepsilon_0 r}$ $E_k = \dfrac{(1\cdot60\times10^{-19})^2}{8\pi\times8\cdot85\times10^{-12}\times0\cdot21\times10^{-9}}$ **(1)** $E_k = 5\cdot5\times10^{-19}$ J **(1)** | 2 | Accept: $5\times10^{-19}$ $5\cdot5\times10^{-19}$ $5\cdot48\times10^{-19}$ $5\cdot483\times10^{-19}$ If $9\times10^9$ used, then accept 5, $5\cdot5$, $5\cdot49$, $5\cdot486$ |
| | (c) | | $mvr = \dfrac{nh}{2\pi}$ **(1)** $4\cdot22\times10^{-34} = \dfrac{n\times6\cdot63\times10^{-34}}{2\pi}$ **(1)** $n = 4$ **(1)(must be integer)** | 3 | |
| | (d) | (i) | $\Delta x\Delta p_x \geq \dfrac{h}{4\pi}$ **(1)** $\Delta x \times 1\cdot5\times10^{-26} \geq \dfrac{6\cdot63\times10^{-34}}{4\pi}$ **(1)** minimum $\Delta x = 3\cdot5\times10^{-9}$ m **(1)** | 3 | Accept: $4\times10^{-9}$, $3\cdot52\times10^{-9}$, $3\cdot517\times10^{-9}$ |
| | | (ii) | $\Delta t\Delta E \geq \dfrac{h}{4\pi}$ **(1)** If $\Delta t$ is small then $\Delta E$ is large. **(1)** Therefore the largest possible energy of the electron may be big enough to overcome the repulsion and cross the gap. **(1)** **OR** $\Delta x\Delta p \geq \dfrac{h}{4\pi}$ **(1)** If the momentum is measured with a small uncertainty, the uncertainty in the position of the electron is large enough **(1)** for the electron to exist on the other side of the gap **(1)**. | 3 | |
| **7.** | (a) | | Reflected wave interferes with transmitted wave (to produce points of destructive and constructive interference). **(1)** | 1 | |
| | (b) | | Antinode (constructive), high energy, so melted spots. **(1)** Node (destructive), low energy, so no melting. **(1)** | 2 | |
| | (c) | | $4\times\dfrac{1}{2}\lambda = 0\cdot264$ m **(1)** $\lambda = 0\cdot132$ m **(1)** | 2 | |

| Question | | | Expected response | Max mark | Additional guidance |
|---|---|---|---|---|---|
| | (d) | | $v = f\lambda$ (1) <br> $= 2\cdot45\times10^{9}\times0\cdot132$ (1) <br> $= 3\cdot234\times10^{8}\,\mathrm{m\,s^{-1}}$ <br> $= 3\cdot23\times10^{8}\,\mathrm{m\,s^{-1}}$ | 2 | If final answer is not shown then maximum of 1 mark only can be awarded. |
| | (e) | | The range of the results is small, so the results are precise. (1) <br><br> The difference between the mean value of the results and the accepted value of c is larger than the range, so the results are not accurate. (1) | 2 | |
| 8. | (a) | | A series of bright and dark spots. | 1 | Accept fringes. |
| | (b) | | $p = mv$ <br> $p = 1\cdot20\times10^{-24}\times220$ <br> $= 2\cdot64\times10^{-22}\,(\mathrm{kg\,m\,s^{-1}})$ <br> $\lambda = \dfrac{h}{p}$ (1)(for both formulae) <br> $= \dfrac{6\cdot63\times10^{-34}}{2\cdot64\times10^{-22}}$ (1)(for both substitutions) <br> $= 2\cdot5\times10^{-12}\,\mathrm{m}$ (1) <br> Estimate in the range of $10^{-12}$ to $10^{-9}$ (1) | 4 | Statement of value of slit separation must be distinct from value of $\lambda$. |
| 9. | (a) | | 3 | 1 | |
| | (b) | | $c = \dfrac{1}{\sqrt{\mu_0\varepsilon_0}}$ (1) <br> $= \dfrac{1}{\sqrt{8\cdot93\times10^{-12}\times1\cdot32\times10^{-6}}}$ (1) <br> $= 2\cdot91\times10^{8}\,\mathrm{m\,s^{-1}}$ (1) | 3 | The answer must be consistent with (a) in terms of significant figures. <br> If not consistent then maximum of 2 marks only can be awarded. |
| | (c) | (i) | %uncert in $\mu_0 = \pm\dfrac{5\times10^{-8}}{1\cdot32\times10^{-6}}\times100$ <br> $= \pm3\cdot8\%$ (1) <br> %uncert in $\varepsilon_0 = \pm\dfrac{7\times10^{-14}}{8\cdot93\times10^{-12}}\times100$ <br> $= \pm0\cdot8\%$ (1) <br> Uncertainty in $\mu_0$ more significant (1) | 3 | |
| | | (ii) | uncert in $\dfrac{1}{\sqrt{\mu_0\varepsilon_0}} = \pm\dfrac{1}{2}\times\dfrac{3\cdot8}{100}\times2\cdot91\times10^{8}$ (1) <br> $= \pm6\times10^{6}\,\mathrm{m\,s^{-1}}$ (1) | 2 | If a candidate combines both uncertainties correctly full marks may be awarded. |

| | Question | | Expected response | Max mark | Additional guidance |
|---|---|---|---|---|---|
| **10.** | (a) | (i) | Force acting per unit positive charge. | 1 | |
| | | (ii) | $\dfrac{Q_1}{4\pi\varepsilon_0 r_1^2} = \dfrac{Q_2}{4\pi\varepsilon_0 r_2^2}$   (1) <br><br> $\dfrac{-8\cdot0\times10^{-9}}{4\pi\varepsilon_0(0\cdot4)^2} = \dfrac{Q_s}{4\pi\varepsilon_0(0\cdot2)^2}$   (1) <br><br> $Q_2 = \dfrac{-8\cdot0\times10^{-9}\times(0\cdot2)^2}{(0\cdot4)^2}$ <br><br> $Q_2 = -2\cdot0\times10^{-9}$ C | 2 | If final answer is not shown then maximum of 1 mark can be awarded. |
| | | (iii) | $V_1 = \dfrac{Q}{4\pi\varepsilon_0 r}$   (1) <br><br> $V_1 = \dfrac{-8\cdot0\times10^{-9}}{4\times\pi\times8\cdot85\times10^{-12}\times0\cdot40}$   (1) <br><br> $V_1 = -180$ V   (1) <br><br> $V_2 = \dfrac{-2\cdot0\times10^{-9}}{4\times\pi\times8\cdot85\times10^{-12}\times0\cdot20}$ <br><br> $V_2 = -90$ V   (1) <br><br> Potential at X $= -180 - 90 = -270$ V   (1) | 5 | $V_1 = -179\cdot84$ <br> $V_2 = -89\cdot92$ |
| | (b) | (i) | $V_1 = \dfrac{-8\cdot0\times10^{-9}}{4\times\pi\times8\cdot85\times10^{-12}\times0\cdot50}$ <br><br> $V_1 = -140$ V   (1) <br><br> $V_2 = \dfrac{-2\cdot0\times10^{-9}}{4\times\pi\times8\cdot85\times10^{-12}\times0\cdot50}$ <br><br> $V_2 = -36$ V   (1) <br><br> Potential at P $= -140 - 36 = -176$ V $= -180$ V   (1) | 3 | Accept: <br> $V_1 = -144$ V <br><br><br><br> Accept: <br> $-176$ V |
| | | (ii) | Potential difference $= -180 - (-270) = 90$ (V)   (1) <br><br> $E = QV$   (1) <br> $= 1\cdot0\times10^{-9}\times90$   (1) <br> $= 9\cdot0\times10^{-8}$ J   (1) | 4 | Accept potential difference $= -176 - (-270) = 94$ V leading to $E = 9\cdot4\times10^{-8}$ J |

| Question | | | Expected response | Additional guidance |
|---|---|---|---|---|
| **11.** | | | The whole candidate response should first be read to establish its overall quality in terms of accuracy and relevance to the problem/situation presented. There may be strengths and weaknesses in the candidate response: assessors should focus as far as possible on the strengths, taking account of weaknesses (errors or omissions) only where they detract from the overall answer in a significant way, which should then be taken into account when determining whether the response demonstrates reasonable, limited or no understanding.<br><br>Assessors should use their professional judgement to apply the guidance below to the wide range of possible candidate responses. | This open-ended question requires comment on the statement "things on a small scale behave nothing like things on a large scale". Candidate responses may include one or more of: macroscopic/microscopic, duality; uncertainty; double slit; failure of Newtonian rules in the atomic world; intuition applies to large objects or other relevant ideas/concepts. |
| | | | **3 marks:** The candidate has demonstrated a **good** conceptual understanding of the physics involved, providing a logically correct response to the problem/situation presented.<br><br>This type of response might include a statement of principle(s) involved, a relationship or equation, and the application of these to respond to the problem/situation.<br><br>This does not mean the answer has to be what might be termed an "excellent answer" or a "complete" one. | In response to this question, a **good** understanding might be demonstrated by a candidate response that:<br>• makes a judgement on suitability based on one relevant physics idea/concept, in a **detailed/developed** response that is **correct or largely correct** (any weaknesses are minor and do not detract from the overall response), **OR**<br>• makes judgement(s) on suitability based on a range of relevant physics ideas/concepts, in a response that is **correct or largely correct** (any weaknesses are minor and do not detract from the overall response), **OR**<br>• otherwise demonstrates a good understanding of the physics involved. |
| | | | **2 marks:** The candidate has demonstrated a **reasonable** understanding of the physics involved, showing that the problem/situation is understood.<br><br>This type of response might make some statement(s) that is/are relevant to the problem/situation, for example, a statement of relevant principle(s) or identification of a relevant relationship or equation. | In response to this question, a **reasonable** understanding might be demonstrated by a candidate response that:<br>• makes a judgement on suitability based on one or more relevant physics idea(s)/concept(s), in a response that is **largely correct** but has **weaknesses** which detract to a small extent from the overall response, **OR**<br>• otherwise demonstrates a reasonable understanding of the physics involved. |

| Question | Expected response | Additional guidance |
|---|---|---|
| | **1 mark:** The candidate has demonstrated a **limited** understanding of the physics involved, showing that a little of the physics that is relevant to the problem/situation is understood.<br><br>The candidate has made some statement(s) that is/are relevant to the problem/situation. | In response to this question, a **limited** understanding might be demonstrated by a candidate response that:<br>• makes a judgement on suitability based on one or more relevant physics idea(s)/concept(s), in a response that has **weaknesses** which detract to a large extent from the overall response, **OR**<br>• otherwise demonstrates a limited understanding of the physics involved. |
| | **0 marks:** The candidate has demonstrated **no** understanding of the physics that is relevant to the problem/situation.<br><br>The candidate has made no statement(s) that is/are relevant to the problem/situation. | Where the candidate has *only* demonstrated knowledge and understanding of physics **that is not relevant to the problem/situation presented,** 0 marks should be awarded. |

| Question | | | Expected response | | Max mark | Additional guidance |
|---|---|---|---|---|---|---|
| **12.** | (a) | (i) | $X_C = \dfrac{1}{2\pi f C}$  $= \dfrac{1}{2 \times \pi \times 65 \times 5\cdot 0 \times 10^{-6}}$  $= 490\,\Omega$ | (1)<br><br>(1)<br><br> | 3 | Accept:<br>500<br>490<br>489·7 |
| | | (ii) | $I_{rms} = \dfrac{V_{rms}}{X_C}$  $= \dfrac{15}{490}$  $= 3\cdot 1 \times 10^{-2}\,A$ | (1)<br><br>(1)<br><br>(1) | 3 | Accept:<br>3<br>3·1<br>3·06<br>3·061 |
| | (b) | (i) | Plot $X_C$ against $1/f$<br>Labels (quantities and units) and scale<br>Points plotted correctly<br>Correct best fit line | (1)<br>(1)<br>(1)<br>(1) | 4 | Non-linear scale a maximum of 1 mark is available.<br>Allow ± half box tolerance when plotting points. |
| | | (ii) | Gradient of best fit line<br>Gradient $= \dfrac{1}{2\pi C}$<br>**OR**<br>$C = \dfrac{1}{(2\pi \times \text{gradient})}$<br><br>Final value of C | (1)<br><br><br><br>(1)<br><br><br>(1) | 3 | If candidates use data points not on their line of best fit, then maximum of 1 mark is available.<br>A representative gradient value of $3\cdot 13 \times 10^7$ gives a capacitance of $5\cdot 08 \times 10^{-9}$ F.<br>Final value of C must be consistent with candidate's value for gradient. |

## ADVANCED HIGHER PHYSICS 2016

| Question | | | Answer | Max mark |
|---|---|---|---|---|
| **1.** | (a) | | $v = 0\cdot135t^2 + 1\cdot26t$ $a = \dfrac{dv}{dt} = 0\cdot135\times2t + 1\cdot26$ **1** $a = (0\cdot135\times2\times15\cdot0)+1\cdot26$ **1** $a = 5\cdot31\,\text{m s}^{-2}$ **1** | 3 |
| | (b) | | $v = 0\cdot135t^2 + 1\cdot26t$ $s = \int_0^{15\cdot0} v\,dt = [0\cdot045t^3 + 0\cdot63t^2]_0^{15\cdot0}$ **1** $s = (0\cdot045\times15\cdot0^3)+(0\cdot63\times15\cdot0^2)$ **1** $s = 294\,\text{m}$ **1** | 3 |
| **2.** | (a) | (i) | Velocity changing Or changing direction Or an unbalanced force is acting Or a centripetal/central/ radial force is acting | 1 |
| | | (ii) | Towards the centre | 1 |
| | (b) | (i) (A) | SHOW QUESTION $\omega = \dfrac{d\theta}{dt}$ OR $\omega = \dfrac{\theta}{t}$ **1** $\omega = \dfrac{1\cdot5\times2\pi}{2\cdot69}$ **1** $\omega = 3\cdot5\,\text{rad s}^{-1}$ | 2 |
| | | (B) | $F = mr\omega^2$ **1** $F = 0\cdot059\times0\cdot48\times3\cdot5^2$ **1** $F = 0\cdot35\,\text{N}$ **1** | 3 |
| | | (C) | $W = mg$ $W = 0\cdot059\times9\cdot8$ **1** $T^2 = 0\cdot35^2 + (0\cdot059\times9\cdot8)^2$ **1** $T = 0\cdot68\,\text{N}$ **1** | 3 |
| | | (ii) | In a straight line at a tangent to the circle | 1 |

| Question | | | Answer | Max mark |
|---|---|---|---|---|
| **3.** | (a) | | $v = \sqrt{\dfrac{2GM}{r}}$ **1** $v = \sqrt{\dfrac{2\times6\cdot67\times10^{-11}\times9\cdot5\times10^{12}}{2\cdot1\times10^3}}$ **1** $v = 0\cdot78\,(\text{m s}^{-1})$ **1** (Lander returns to surface as) lander v less than escape velocity of comet **1** | 4 |
| | (b) | (i) | SHOW QUESTION $(F_g = W)$ $\dfrac{GMm}{r^2} = mg$ **1** for both eqns, **1** for equating $g = \dfrac{GM}{r^2}$ $g = \dfrac{6\cdot67\times10^{-11}\times9\cdot5\times10^{12}}{(2\cdot1\times10^3)^2}$ **1** $g = 1\cdot4\times10^{-4}\,\text{N kg}^{-1}$ | 3 |
| | | (ii) | Height will be greater **1** Because '$a$' reduces **1** with height **1** | 3 |
| **4.** | (a) | | $b = \dfrac{L}{4\pi r^2}$ **1** $1\cdot05\times10^{-9} = \dfrac{L}{4\pi(9\cdot94\times10^{16})^2}$ **1** $L = 1\cdot30\times10^{26}\,\text{W}$ **1** | 3 |
| | (b) | | $L = 4\pi r^2\sigma T^4$ **1** $1\cdot30\times10^{26} = 4\pi(5\cdot10\times10^8)^2$ $\times5\cdot67\times10^{-8}\times T^4$ **1** $T = 5150\,\text{K}$ **1** | 3 |
| | (c) | | That the star is a black body (emitter/radiator) OR The star is spherical/ constant radius OR The surface temperature of the star is constant/uniform OR No energy absorbed between star and Earth | 1 |

| Question | | | Answer | Max mark |
|---|---|---|---|---|
| 5. | (a) | (i) | Frames of reference that are accelerating (with respect to an inertial frame) | 1 |
| | | (ii) | It is impossible to tell the difference between the effects of gravity and acceleration. | 1 |
| | (b) | (i) | Any convex upward parabola | 1 |
| | | (ii) | Any straight line | 1 |
| | (c) | | The clock on the surface of the Earth would run more slowly.    **1** <br><br> The (effective) gravitational field for the spacecraft is smaller.    **1** <br><br> **OR** vice versa | 2 |
| 6. | | | This is an open-ended question. <br><br> Demonstrates no understanding    0 marks <br><br> Demonstrates limited understanding    1 mark <br><br> Demonstrates reasonable understanding    2 marks <br><br> Demonstrates good understanding    3 marks <br><br> **1 mark:** The student has demonstrated a limited understanding of the physics involved. The student has made some statement(s) which is/are relevant to the situation, showing that at least a little of the physics within the problem is understood. | 3 |

| Question | | | Answer | | Max mark |
|---|---|---|---|---|---|
| | | | **2 marks:** The student has demonstrated a reasonable understanding of the physics involved. The student makes some statement(s) which is/are relevant to the situation, showing that the problem is understood. <br><br> **3 marks:** The maximum available mark would be awarded to a student who has demonstrated a good understanding of the physics involved. The student shows a good comprehension of the physics of the situation and has provided a logically correct answer to the question posed. This type of response might include a statement of the principles involved, a relationship or an equation, and the application of these to respond to the problem. This does not mean the answer has to be what might be termed an "excellent" answer or a "complete" one. | | |
| 7. | (a) | (i) | $T_K = 15 + 273$     1 <br><br> $T_{kelvin} = \dfrac{b}{\lambda_{peak}}$ <br><br> $288 = \dfrac{2 \cdot 89 x 10^{-3}}{\lambda_{peak}}$     1 <br><br> $\lambda_{peak} = 1 \cdot 0 \times 10^{-5}$ m     1 | | 3 |
| | | (ii) | Infrared | 1 | |
| | (b) | (i) | (Curve) A     1 <br> Peak at shorter wavelength/higher frequency (as temperature is higher)     1 <br> **OR** <br> Higher/greater (peak) intensity (as greater energy)     1 | | 2 |

| Question | | | Answer | Max mark |
|---|---|---|---|---|
| | | (ii) | Curve asymptotic to y-axis and decreasing with increased wavelength | 1 |
| **8.** | (a) | (i) | The uncertainty in the momentum (in the x-direction) | 1 |
| | | (ii) | The precise position of a particle/system and its momentum cannot both be known at the same instant. **1** <br><br> **OR** <br><br> If the uncertainty in the location of the particle is reduced, the minimum uncertainty in the momentum of the particle will increase (or vice-versa). **1** <br><br> **OR** <br><br> The precise energy and lifetime of a particle cannot both be known at the same instant. **1** <br><br> **OR** <br><br> If the uncertainty in the energy of the particle is reduced, the minimum uncertainty in the lifetime of the particle will increase (or vice-versa). **1** | 1 |
| | (b) | (i) | $\lambda = \dfrac{h}{p}$  **1** <br><br> $\lambda = \dfrac{6 \cdot 63 \times 10^{-34}}{6 \cdot 5 \times 10^{-24}}$  **1** <br><br> $\lambda = 1 \cdot 0 \times 10^{-10}$ (m)  **1** <br><br> slit width $0 \cdot 1$ nm used  **1** | 4 |
| | | (ii) | $\Delta x \, \Delta p_x \geq \dfrac{h}{4\pi}$  **1** <br><br> $\Delta x \times 6 \cdot 5 \times 10^{-26} \geq \dfrac{6 \cdot 63 \times 10^{-34}}{4\pi}$  **1** <br><br> $\Delta x \geq 8 \cdot 1 \times 10^{-10}$ <br> min uncertainty <br> $= 8 \cdot 1 \times 10^{-10}$ m  **1** | 3 |

| Question | | | Answer | Max mark |
|---|---|---|---|---|
| | (b) | (iii) | Electron behaves like a wave <br><br> "Electron shows interference" <br><br> Uncertainty in position is greater than slit separation <br><br> Electron passes through both slits <br><br> Any three of the statements can be awarded 1 mark each | 3 |
| **9.** | (a) | | SHOW QUESTION <br><br> $m\dfrac{v^2}{r} = Bqv$ <br><br> 1 for both relationships <br> 1 for equating <br><br> $r = \dfrac{mv}{Bq}$ | 2 |
| | (b) | (i) | $1 \cdot 50$ (MeV) <br> $= 1 \cdot 50 \times 10^6$ <br> $\times \, 1 \cdot 60 \times 10^{-19}$ <br> $= 2 \cdot 40 \times 10^{-13}$ (J)  **1** <br><br> $E_k = \dfrac{1}{2} mv^2$  **1** <br><br> $2 \cdot 40 \times 10^{-13} = 0 \cdot 5 \times 3 \cdot 34$ $\times \, 10^{-27} \times v^2$  **1** <br> $v = 1 \cdot 20 \times 10^7$ ms$^{-1}$  **1** | 4 |
| | | (ii) | $r = \dfrac{mv}{Bq}$ <br><br> $2 \cdot 50 = \dfrac{3 \cdot 34 \times 10^{-27} \times 1 \cdot 20 \times 10^7}{B \times 1 \cdot 60 \times 10^{-19}}$  **1** <br> $B = 0 \cdot 100$ T  **1** | 2 |
| | | (iii) | r will be less  **1** <br><br> $r \propto \dfrac{m}{q}$ <br><br> **and** <br> q increases more than m does or q doubles but m increases by a factor of $1 \cdot 5$  **1** | 2 |
| **10.** | (a) | (i) | Displacement is proportional to and in the opposite direction to the acceleration. | 1 |

| Question | | | Answer | Max mark |
|---|---|---|---|---|
| | | (ii) | SHOW QUESTION<br><br>$y = A\cos \omega t$<br><br>$\dfrac{dy}{dt} = -\omega A \sin \omega t$<br><br>$\dfrac{d^2 y}{dt^2} = -\omega^2 A\cos \omega t$    1<br><br>$\dfrac{d^2 y}{dt^2} = -\omega^2 y$    1<br><br>$\dfrac{d^2 y}{dt^2} + \omega^2 y = 0$ | 2 |
| | (b) | (i) | SHOW QUESTION<br><br>$T = \dfrac{12\cdot 0}{10}$    1<br><br>$\omega = \dfrac{2\pi}{T}$    1<br><br>$\omega = \dfrac{2\pi \times 10}{12}$    1<br><br>$\omega = 5\cdot 2 \text{ rad s}^{-1}$ | 3 |
| | | (ii) | $v = (\pm)\omega\sqrt{A^2 - y^2}$    1<br><br>$v = 5\cdot 2 \times 0\cdot 04$    1<br><br>$v = 0\cdot 21 \text{ m s}^{-1}$    1 | 3 |
| | | (iii) | $E_P = \dfrac{1}{2}m\omega^2 y^2$    1<br><br>$E_P = \dfrac{1}{2} \times 1\cdot 5 \times 5\cdot 2^2 \times 0\cdot 04^2$    1<br><br>$E_P = 0\cdot 032 \text{ J}$    1 | 3 |
| | (c) | (i) | Any valid method of damping | 1 |
| | | (ii) | Amplitude of harmonic wave reducing | 1 |
| 11. | (a) | | $\dfrac{1}{\lambda} = 0\cdot 357$    1<br><br>$\lambda = \dfrac{1}{0\cdot 357}$<br><br>$v = f\lambda$    1<br><br>$v = 118 \times \dfrac{1}{0\cdot 357}$    1<br><br>$v = 331 \text{ m s}^{-1}$    1 | 4 |

| Question | | | Answer | Max mark |
|---|---|---|---|---|
| | (b) | | $E = kA^2$    1<br><br>$\dfrac{E_1}{A_1^2} = \dfrac{E_2}{A_2^2}$<br><br>$\dfrac{1}{0\cdot 250^2} = \dfrac{0\cdot 5}{A_2^2}$    1<br><br>$A_2 = 0\cdot 177 \text{ (m)}$    1<br><br>$\Delta y = 0\cdot 177\sin 2\pi\,(118t + 0\cdot 357x)$    1 | 4 |
| 12. | (a) | | (The axes should be arranged) at $90°$ to each other (e.g. horizontal and vertical). | 1 |
| | (b) | | The filter for each eye will allow light from one projected image to pass through    1<br><br>while blocking the light from the other projector.    1 | 2 |
| | (c) | | There will be no change to the brightness.    1<br><br>Light from the lamp is unpolarised.    1 | 2 |
| | (d) | | (As the student rotates the filter,) the image from one projector will decrease in brightness, while the image from the other projector will increase in brightness. (The two images are almost identical.)    1 | 1 |
| 13. | (a) | | SHOW QUESTION<br><br>$V = \dfrac{1}{4\pi\varepsilon_o}\dfrac{Q_1}{r}$    1<br><br>$V = \dfrac{1}{4\pi \times 8\cdot 85 \times 10^{-12}}\dfrac{12 \times 10^{-9}}{0\cdot 30}$    1<br><br>$V = (+)360 \text{ V}$ | 2 |

| Question | | | Answer | Max mark |
|---|---|---|---|---|
| (b) | (i) | | $V = -360$ (V)  1 $$V = \frac{1}{4\pi\varepsilon_o}\frac{Q_2}{r}$$ $$-360 = \frac{Q_2}{4\pi \times 8\cdot85 \times 10^{-12} \times 0\cdot40} \quad 1$$ $Q_2 = -1\cdot6 \times 10^{-8}$ C  1 | 3 |
| | (ii) | | $$E_1 = \frac{1}{4\pi\varepsilon_o}\frac{Q_1}{r^2} \quad 1$$ $$E_1 = \frac{1}{4\pi \times 8\cdot85 \times 10^{-12}}\frac{12 \times 10^{-9}}{0\cdot30^2} \quad 1$$ $E_1 = 1200$  (N C$^{-1}$ to right) $$E_2 = \frac{1}{4\pi \times 8\cdot85 \times 10^{-12}}\frac{1\cdot6 \times 10^{-8}}{0\cdot40^2} \quad 1$$ $E_2 = 900$  (N C$^{-1}$ to right) $Total = 2100$  N C$^{-1}$ (to right) 1 | 4 |
| | (iii) | | Shape of attractive field, including correct direction  1 | 2 |
| | | | Skew in correct direction  1 | |
| 14. | (a) | | $$B = \frac{\mu_o I}{2\pi r} \quad 1$$ $$B = 5 \times 10^{-6} = \frac{4\pi \times 10^{-7} \times I}{2\pi \times 0\cdot1} \quad 1$$ $I = 2\cdot5$ A  1 | 3 |
| | (b) | (i) | Ignore calibration (less than 1/3) $$\%u/c = \frac{0\cdot002}{0\cdot1} \times 100 = 2\% \quad 1$$ | 1 |
| | | (ii) | Reading $5 = \frac{0\cdot1}{5} \times 100 = 2\%$  1 Total% = $\sqrt{(\text{reading}\%^2 + \text{calibration}\%^2)}$  1 Total % $= \sqrt{(1\cdot5^2 + 2^2)}$ $= 2\cdot5\%$  1 | 3 |

| Question | | | Answer | Max mark |
|---|---|---|---|---|
| | | (iii) | Total % $= \sqrt{(2^2 + 2\cdot5^2)}$ $= \sqrt{10\cdot25}\%$  1 abs u/c $= \dfrac{\sqrt{10\cdot25}}{100} \times 2\cdot5$  1 $= 0\cdot08$ A | 2 |
| | (c) | | Uncertainty in measuring exact distance from wire to position of sensor | 1 |
| 15. | (a) | (i) | $gradient = \dfrac{8\cdot3 \times 10^{-10}}{10^3}$ $= 8\cdot3 \times 10^{-13}$  1 $\cdots\cdots\cdots\cdots\cdots\cdots\cdots\cdots$ $gradient = \varepsilon_0 A$ $8\cdot3 \times 10^{-13} = \varepsilon_0 \times 9\cdot0 \times 10^{-2}$  1 $\varepsilon_0 = 9\cdot2 \times 10^{-12}$ F m$^{-1}$  1 | 3 |
| | | (ii) | $$c = \frac{1}{\sqrt{\varepsilon_0\mu_0}} \quad 1$$ $$c = \frac{1}{\sqrt{9\cdot2 \times 10^{-12} \times 4\pi \times 10^{-7}}} \quad 1$$ $c = 2\cdot9 \times 10^8$ m s$^{-1}$  1 | 3 |
| | (b) | | Systematic uncertainty specific to capacitance or spacing measurement | 1 |
| 16. | (a) | | $$I = \frac{2}{5}mr^2 \quad 1$$ $$I = \frac{2}{5} \times 3\cdot8 \times 0\cdot053^2 \quad 1$$ $I = 4\cdot3 \times 10^{-3}$ kg m$^2$  1 | 3 |
| | (b) | (i) | Labelling & scales  1 Plotting  1 Best fit line  1 | 3 |
| | | (ii) | $gradient = 1\cdot73$ or consistent with candidate's best fit line  1 $\cdots\cdots\cdots\cdots\cdots\cdots\cdots\cdots$ $$2gh = \left(\frac{I}{mr^2} + 1\right)v^2$$ $$\frac{2gh}{v^2} = \left(\frac{I}{mr^2} + 1\right)$$ $$1\cdot73 = \left(\frac{I}{3\cdot8 \times 0\cdot053^2} + 1\right) \quad 1$$ $I = 7\cdot8 \times 10^{-3}$ kgm$^2$  1 | 3 |

| Question | | | Answer | Max mark |
|---|---|---|---|---|
| | (c) | | This is an open-ended question. | 3 |
| | | | Demonstrates no understanding       0 marks | |
| | | | Demonstrates limited understanding       1 mark | |
| | | | Demonstrates reasonable understanding       2 marks | |
| | | | Demonstrates good understanding       3 marks | |
| | | | **1 mark:** The student has demonstrated a limited understanding of the physics involved. The student has made some statement(s) which is/are relevant to the situation, showing that at least a little of the physics within the problem is understood. | |
| | | | **2 marks:** The student has demonstrated a reasonable understanding of the physics involved. The student makes some statement(s) which is/are relevant to the situation, showing that the problem is understood. | |
| | | | **3 marks:** The maximum available mark would be awarded to a student who has demonstrated a good understanding of the physics involved. The student sh ows a good comprehension of the physics of the situation and has provided a logically correct answer to the question posed. | |

| Question | | | Answer | Max mark |
|---|---|---|---|---|
| | | | This type of response might include a statement of the principles involved, a relationship or an equation, and the application of these to respond to the problem. This does not mean the answer has to be what might be termed an "excellent" answer or a "complete" one. | |

## ADVANCED HIGHER PHYSICS 2017

| Question | | | Answer | Max mark |
|---|---|---|---|---|
| 1. | (a) | | $v = 0\cdot4t^2 + 2t$<br>$v = (0\cdot4 \times 3\cdot10^2)$<br>$\qquad + (2 \times 3\cdot10)$ **1**<br>$v = 10\cdot0\ \mathrm{ms^{-1}}$ **1**<br>Accept: 10, 10·04, 10·044 | 2 |
| | (b) | | $s = \int\left(0\cdot4t^2 + 2t\right).dt$<br>$s = \dfrac{0\cdot4}{3}t^3 + t^2 (+c)$ **1**<br>$s = 0$ when $t = 0$, $c = 0$<br>$s = \dfrac{0\cdot4}{3} \times (3\cdot10)^3 + 3\cdot10^2$ **1**<br>$s = 13\cdot6\,\mathrm{m}$ **1**<br>Accept: 14, 13·58, 13·582 | 3 |
| 2. | (a) | (i) | 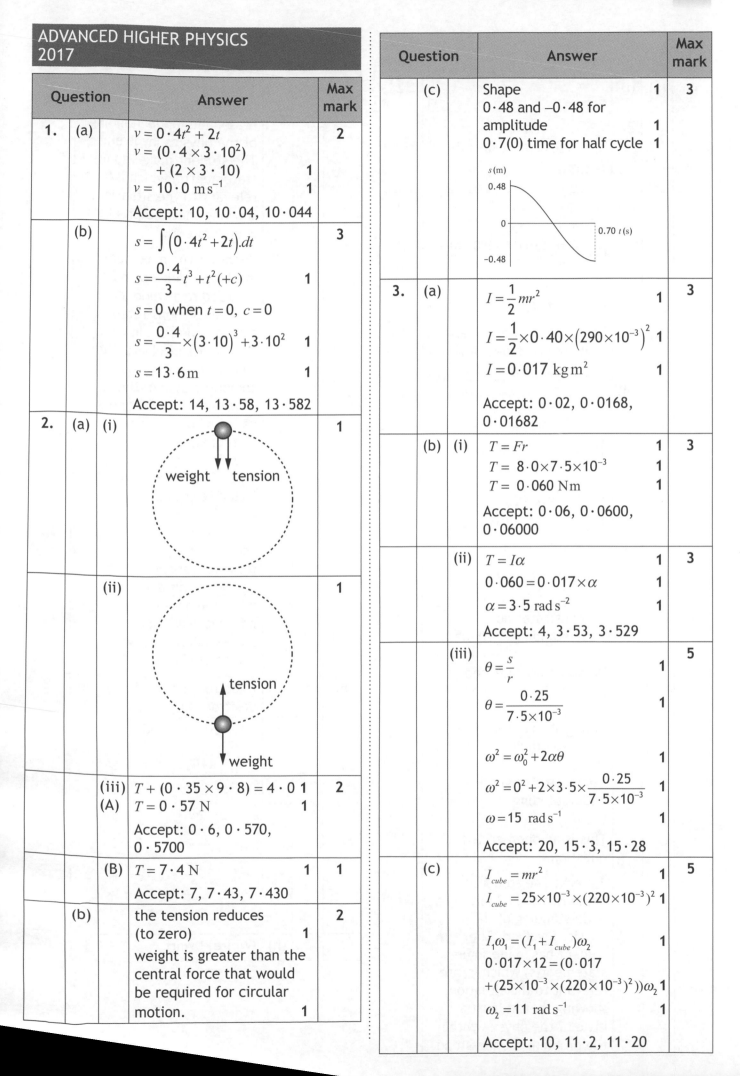 weight    tension | 1 |
| | | (ii) | tension<br>weight | 1 |
| | | (iii)<br>(A) | $T + (0\cdot35 \times 9\cdot8) = 4\cdot01$ **1**<br>$T = 0\cdot57\,\mathrm{N}$ **1**<br>Accept: 0·6, 0·570, 0·5700 | 2 |
| | | (B) | $T = 7\cdot4\,\mathrm{N}$ **1**<br>Accept: 7, 7·43, 7·430 | 1 |
| | (b) | | the tension reduces (to zero) **1**<br>weight is greater than the central force that would be required for circular motion. **1** | 2 |

| Question | | | Answer | Max mark |
|---|---|---|---|---|
| | (c) | | Shape **1**<br>0·48 and −0·48 for amplitude **1**<br>0·7(0) time for half cycle **1**<br><br>$s$(m)<br>0.48<br>0<br>−0.48  0.70 $t$(s) | 3 |
| 3. | (a) | | $I = \dfrac{1}{2}mr^2$ **1**<br>$I = \dfrac{1}{2} \times 0\cdot40 \times (290 \times 10^{-3})^2$ **1**<br>$I = 0\cdot017\ \mathrm{kgm^2}$ **1**<br>Accept: 0·02, 0·0168, 0·01682 | 3 |
| | (b) | (i) | $T = Fr$ **1**<br>$T = 8\cdot0 \times 7\cdot5 \times 10^{-3}$ **1**<br>$T = 0\cdot060\ \mathrm{Nm}$ **1**<br>Accept: 0·06, 0·0600, 0·06000 | 3 |
| | | (ii) | $T = I\alpha$ **1**<br>$0\cdot060 = 0\cdot017 \times \alpha$ **1**<br>$\alpha = 3\cdot5\ \mathrm{rad\,s^{-2}}$ **1**<br>Accept: 4, 3·53, 3·529 | 3 |
| | | (iii) | $\theta = \dfrac{s}{r}$ **1**<br>$\theta = \dfrac{0\cdot25}{7\cdot5 \times 10^{-3}}$ **1**<br>$\omega^2 = \omega_0^2 + 2\alpha\theta$ **1**<br>$\omega^2 = 0^2 + 2 \times 3\cdot5 \times \dfrac{0\cdot25}{7\cdot5 \times 10^{-3}}$ **1**<br>$\omega = 15\ \mathrm{rad\,s^{-1}}$ **1**<br>Accept: 20, 15·3, 15·28 | 5 |
| | (c) | | $I_{cube} = mr^2$ **1**<br>$I_{cube} = 25 \times 10^{-3} \times (220 \times 10^{-3})^2$ **1**<br>$I_1\omega_1 = (I_1 + I_{cube})\omega_2$ **1**<br>$0\cdot017 \times 12 = (0\cdot017 + (25 \times 10^{-3} \times (220 \times 10^{-3})^2))\omega_2$ **1**<br>$\omega_2 = 11\ \mathrm{rad\,s^{-1}}$ **1**<br>Accept: 10, 11·2, 11·20 | 5 |

| Question | | | Answer | | Max mark |
|---|---|---|---|---|---|
| 4. | (a) | (i) | $F = \dfrac{mv^2}{r}$ | 1 | 2 |
| | | | $24 \cdot 1 = \dfrac{1240 \times v^2}{(263 \times 10^3 + 680 \times 10^3)}$ | 1 | |
| | | | $v = 135 \text{ m s}^{-1}$ | | |
| | | (ii) | $v_c = \dfrac{2\pi r}{T}$ | 1 | 3 |
| | | | $135 = \dfrac{2\pi(263 \times 10^3 + 680 \times 10^3)}{T}$ | 1 | |
| | | | $T = 4 \cdot 39 \times 10^4 \text{ s}$ | 1 | |
| | | | Accept: $4 \cdot 4$, $4 \cdot 389$, $4 \cdot 3889$ | | |
| | (b) | (i) | The work done in moving unit mass from infinity (to that point). | 1 | 1 |
| | | (ii) | $V_{low} - V_{high} = -3 \cdot 22 \times 10^4$ $-(-1 \cdot 29 \times 10^4)$ | 1 | 4 |
| | | | $V_{low} - V_{high} = -1 \cdot 93 \times 10^4$ | | |
| | | | $(\Delta)E = (\Delta)Vm$ | 1 | |
| | | | $(\Delta)E = -1 \cdot 93 \times 10^4 \times 1240$ | 1 | |
| | | | $(\Delta)E = -2 \cdot 39 \times 10^7 \text{ J}$ | 1 | |
| | | | Accept: $2 \cdot 4$, $2 \cdot 393$, $2 \cdot 3932$ | | |
| 5. | | | Demonstrates no understanding 0 marks | | 3 |
| | | | Demonstrates limited understanding 1 mark | | |
| | | | Demonstrates reasonable understanding 2 marks | | |
| | | | Demonstrates good understanding 3 marks | | |
| | | | This is an open-ended question. | | |
| | | | **1 mark:** The student has demonstrated a limited understanding of the physics involved. The student has made some statement(s) which is/are relevant to the situation, showing that at least a little of the physics within the problem is understood. | | |

| Question | | | Answer | | Max mark |
|---|---|---|---|---|---|
| | | | **2 marks:** The student has demonstrated a reasonable understanding of the physics involved. The student makes some statement(s) which is/are relevant to the situation, showing that the problem is understood. | | |
| | | | **3 marks:** The maximum available mark would be awarded to a student who has demonstrated a good understanding of the physics involved. The student shows a good comprehension of the physics of the situation and has provided a logically correct answer to the question posed. This type of response might include a statement of the principles involved, a relationship or an equation, and the application of these to respond to the problem. This does not mean the answer has to be what might be termed an "excellent" answer or a "complete" one. | | |
| 6. | (a) | | (electron) neutrino (1) and positron (1) | | 2 |
| | (b) | (i) | Correctly marked 1 | | 1 |
| | | | | | |
| | | (ii) | (White) Dwarf 1 | | 1 |

| Question | | | Answer | | Max mark |
|---|---|---|---|---|---|
| | | (iii) | $L = 4\cdot9\times10^{-4}\times3\cdot9\times10^{26}$ $\quad$ 1 | | 4 |
| | | | $b = \dfrac{L}{4\pi r^2}$ $\qquad$ 1 | | |
| | | | $1\cdot3\times10^{-12}$ | | |
| | | | $= \dfrac{4\cdot9\times10^{-4}\times3\cdot9\times10^{26}}{4\pi r^2}$ $\quad$ 1 | | |
| | | | $r = 1\cdot1\times10^{17}$ m $\qquad$ 1 | | |
| | | | Accept: 1, $1\cdot08$, $1\cdot082$ | | |
| | (c) | | $\dfrac{L}{L_0} = 1\cdot5\left(\dfrac{M}{M_0}\right)^{3\cdot5}$ | | 2 |
| | | | $\dfrac{L}{L_0} = 1\cdot5\left(\dfrac{10\cdot3}{1}\right)^{3\cdot5}$ $\quad$ 1 | | |
| | | | $L = 5260\left(L_0\right)$ $\qquad$ 1 | | |
| | | | Accept: 5300, $5260\cdot4$ | | |
| 7. | (a) | | Atoms in the Nd:YAG have a shorter lifetime (in the excited state) OR Atoms in the Ar have a longer lifetime (in the excited state) $\qquad$ 1 | | 2 |
| | | | $\Delta f \propto \Delta E$ and $\Delta t \propto \dfrac{1}{\Delta E}$ or $\Delta t \propto \dfrac{1}{\Delta f}$ $\qquad$ 1 | | |
| | (b) | (i) | $\Delta E \Delta t \geq \dfrac{h}{4\pi}$ $\qquad$ 1 | | 3 |
| | | | $\Delta E_{(min)} \times 5\cdot0\times10^{-6}$ | | |
| | | | $= \dfrac{6\cdot63\times10^{-34}}{4\pi}$ $\qquad$ 1 | | |
| | | | $\Delta E_{(min)} = 1\cdot1\times10^{-29}$ J $\quad$ 1 | | |
| | | | Accept: 1, $1\cdot06$, $1\cdot055$ | | |
| | | (ii) | $(\Delta)E = h(\Delta)f$ $\qquad$ 1 | | 3 |
| | | | $1\cdot1\times10^{-29} = 6\cdot63\times10^{-34}$ $\times(\Delta)f$ $\qquad$ 1 | | |
| | | | $(\Delta)f = 1\cdot7\times10^4$ Hz $\quad$ 1 | | |
| | | | Accept: 2, $1\cdot66$, $1\cdot659$ | | |

| Question | | | Answer | | Max mark |
|---|---|---|---|---|---|
| 8. | (a) | | At $t = 0$ $\sin\omega t = 0$, which would mean that $y = 0$. This is not the case in the example here, where $y = A$ at $t = 0$ $\qquad$ 1 | | 1 |
| | (b) | (i) | $(F =)(-)m\omega^2 y = (-)ky$ $\quad$ 1 | | 2 |
| | | | $\omega^2 = \dfrac{ky}{my}$ | | |
| | | | $\omega = \sqrt{\dfrac{k}{m}}$ | | |
| | | | $\omega = 2\pi f$ $\qquad$ 1 | | |
| | | | $2\pi f = \sqrt{\dfrac{k}{m}}$ | | |
| | | | $f = \dfrac{1}{2\pi}\sqrt{\dfrac{k}{m}}$ | | |
| | | (ii) | $f = \dfrac{1}{T} = \left(\dfrac{1}{0\cdot80}\right)$ $\quad$ 1 | | 3 |
| | | | $f = \dfrac{1}{2\pi}\sqrt{\dfrac{k}{m}}$ | | |
| | | | $\dfrac{1}{0\cdot80} = \dfrac{1}{2\pi}\sqrt{\dfrac{k}{0\cdot50}}$ $\quad$ 1 | | |
| | | | $k = 31\,\text{N m}^{-1}$ $\qquad$ 1 | | |
| | | | Accept: 30, $30\cdot8$, $30\cdot84$ | | |
| | | (iii) | $T = \dfrac{0\cdot80}{\sqrt{2}}$ $\qquad$ 1 | | 2 |
| | | | $T = 0\cdot57$ s $\qquad$ 1 | | |
| | | | Accept: $0\cdot6$, $0\cdot566$, $0\cdot5657$ | | |
| | (c) | | | | 2 |
| 9. | (a) | (i) | $(\omega = 2\pi f)$ | | 1 |
| | | | $922 = 2\pi f$ $\qquad$ 1 | | |
| | | | $f = 147$ Hz | | |

| Question | | | Answer | Max mark |
|---|---|---|---|---|
| | | (ii) | $4 \cdot 50 = \left(\dfrac{2\pi}{\lambda}\right)$  **1**<br><br>$v = f\lambda$  **1**<br><br>$v = 147 \times \left(\dfrac{2\pi}{4 \cdot 50}\right)$  **1**<br><br>$v = 205 \ \mathrm{m\,s^{-1}}$  **1**<br><br>Accept: 210, 205·3, 205·25 | 4 |
| | | (iii) | $E = kA^2$  **1**<br><br>$\dfrac{E}{(9 \cdot 50 \times 10^{-4})^2} = \dfrac{E}{8 \times A^2}$  **1**<br><br>$A = 3 \cdot 36 \times 10^{-4} \ \mathrm{m}$  **1**<br><br>Accept: 3·4, 3·359, 3·3588 | 3 |
| | (b) | | $\mu = \dfrac{9 \cdot 0 \times 10^{-3}}{0 \cdot 69}$  **1**<br><br>$v = \sqrt{\dfrac{T}{\mu}}$<br><br>$203 = \sqrt{\dfrac{T}{\left(\dfrac{9 \cdot 0 \times 10^{-3}}{0 \cdot 69}\right)}}$  **1**<br><br>$T = 540 \ \mathrm{N}$  **1**<br><br>Accept: 500, 538, 537·5 | 3 |
| | (c) | (i) | Waves <u>reflected</u> from each end <u>interfere</u> (to create maxima and minima).  **1**  **1** | 1 |
| | | (ii) | $f_3 = (3 \times 270 =) 810 \ \mathrm{Hz}$  **1** | 1 |
| 10. | (a) | | Pattern produced by <u>interference</u>.  **1**<br><br>Slits <u>horizontal and vertical</u> or at <u>right angles</u>  **1** | 2 |
| | (b) | | The spots are closer together.  **1**<br><br>The green light has a shorter wavelength and since $d\sin\theta = m\lambda$, $d$ is fixed, $(\sin)\theta$ is smaller.  **1** | 2 |

| Question | | | Answer | Max mark |
|---|---|---|---|---|
| | (c) | (i) | $\Delta x = \dfrac{\lambda D}{d}$  **1**<br><br>$13 \cdot 0 \times 10^{-3} = \dfrac{\lambda \times 8 \cdot 11}{0 \cdot 41 \times 10^{-3}}$  **1**<br><br>$\lambda = 6 \cdot 6 \times 10^{-7} \ \mathrm{m}$  **1**<br><br>Accept: 7, 6·57, 6·572 | 3 |
| | | (ii) | % Uncertainty in fringe separation<br>$= \left(\dfrac{0 \cdot 5}{13 \cdot 0}\right) \times 100$  **1**<br>$= 3 \cdot 85\%$<br><br>% Uncertainty in slit separation<br>$= \left(\dfrac{0 \cdot 01}{0 \cdot 41}\right) \times 100$  **1**<br>$= 2 \cdot 44\%$<br><br>% Uncertainty in slit-screen separation<br>$= \left(\dfrac{0 \cdot 01}{8 \cdot 11}\right) \times 100$  **1**<br>$= 0 \cdot 123\%$<br>(can be ignored)<br><br>% uncertainty in wavelength<br>$= \sqrt{\left(\dfrac{0 \cdot 5}{13 \cdot 0}\right)^2 + \left(\dfrac{0 \cdot 01}{0 \cdot 41}\right)^2} \times 100\%$<br>$= 4 \cdot 56\%$  **1**<br><br>$\Delta\lambda = \dfrac{4 \cdot 56}{100} \times 6 \cdot 6 \times 10^{-7}$<br>$\Delta\lambda = 0 \cdot 3 \times 10^{-7} \ \mathrm{m}$  **1** | 5 |
| | | (iii) | Increasing the slit-screen distance spreads out the fringes, <u>reducing the</u> (percentage) <u>uncertainty in the fringe separation</u> (which is the dominant uncertainty).  **1** | 1 |
| 11. | (a) | | Force acting per unit positive charge (in an electric field)  **1** | 1 |

| Question | | | Answer | | Max mark |
|---|---|---|---|---|---|
| | (b) | (i) | $E = \dfrac{Q}{4\pi\varepsilon_0 r^2}$ | 1 | 3 |
| | | | $E = \dfrac{4 \cdot 0 \times 10^{-9}}{4\pi \times 8 \cdot 85 \times 10^{-12} \times 0 \cdot 12^2}$ | 1 | |
| | | | $E_{total} = \sqrt{2 \times \left[\dfrac{4 \cdot 0 \times 10^{-9}}{4\pi \times 8 \cdot 85 \times 10^{-12} \times 0 \cdot 12^2}\right]^2}$ | 1 | |
| | | | $E_{total} = 3 \cdot 5 \times 10^3 \, \text{N C}^{-1}$ | | |
| | | (ii) | $F = QE$ | 1 | 3 |
| | | | $F = 1 \cdot 9 \times 10^{-9} \times 3 \cdot 5 \times 10^3$ | 1 | |
| | | | $F = 6 \cdot 7 \times 10^{-6} \, \text{N}$ | 1 | |
| | | | Accept: 7, 6·65, 6·650 | | |
| | | (iii) | Towards the top of the page. | 1 | 1 |
| | | (iv) | $r = \sqrt{(0 \cdot 12^2 + 0 \cdot 12^2)}$ | 1 | 4 |
| | | | $F = \dfrac{Q_1 Q_2}{4\pi\varepsilon_0 r^2}$ | 1 | |
| | | | $6 \cdot 7 \times 10^{-6}$ | | |
| | | | $= \dfrac{1 \cdot 9 \times 10^{-9} \times Q_2}{4\pi \times 8 \cdot 85 \times 10^{-12} \times \sqrt{(0 \cdot 12^2 + 0 \cdot 12^2)}^2}$ | 1 | |
| | | | $Q_2 = 1 \cdot 1 \times 10^{-8} \, \text{C}$ | 1 | |
| | | | Accept: 1, 1·13, 1·129 | | |
| 12. | (a) | | Towards the top of the page. | 1 | 1 |
| | (b) | | $F = qvB$ | 1 | 3 |
| | | | $4 \cdot 00 \times 10^{-15} = 1 \cdot 60 \times 10^{-19}$ | | |
| | | | $\times v \times 115 \times 10^{-3}$ | 1 | |
| | | | $v = 2 \cdot 17 \times 10^5 \, \text{m s}^{-1}$ | 1 | |
| | | | Accept: 2·2, 2·174, 2·1739 | | |
| | (c) | | (Since $F = Bqv$) At lower speeds the magnetic force is reduced. | 1 | 2 |
| | | | Therefore unbalanced force (or acceleration) is downwards Or The magnetic force is less than the electric force | 1 | |
| | (d) | | (All undeflected ions travel at) $2 \cdot 17 \times 10^5 \, \text{m s}^{-1}$ | 1 | 2 |
| | | | relative size of forces is independent of mass and of charge. | 1 | |

| Question | | | Answer | | Max mark |
|---|---|---|---|---|---|
| 13. | (a) | | $t = RC$ | 1 | 2 |
| | | | $t = 1 \cdot 0 \times 10^3 \times 1 \cdot 0$ | 1 | |
| | | | $t = 1 \cdot 0 \times 10^3 \, \text{s}$ | | |
| | (b) | (i) | circuit diagram showing (12V) d.c. supply, resistor and capacitor all in series. Values not required. | | 1 |
| | | | Voltmeter or CRO connected across the capacitor. | 1 | |
| | | (ii) (A) | (After 1 time constant or 1000 s) $V = 7 \cdot 6 \, (V)$ | 1 | 2 |
| | | | $\dfrac{V_c}{V_s} = \dfrac{7 \cdot 6}{12}$ | 1 | |
| | | | $\dfrac{V_c}{V_s} = 63\%$ | | |
| | | (ii) (B) | $4 \cdot 5 - 5$ | 1 | 1 |
| | (c) | | Demonstrates no understanding    0 marks | | 3 |
| | | | Demonstrates limited understanding    1 mark | | |
| | | | Demonstrates reasonable understanding    2 marks | | |
| | | | Demonstrates good understanding    3 marks | | |
| | | | This is an open-ended question. | | |
| | | | **1 mark:** The student has demonstrated a limited understanding of the physics involved. The student has made some statement(s) which is/are relevant to the situation, showing that at least a little of the physics within the problem is understood. | | |
| | | | **2 marks:** The student has demonstrated a reasonable understanding of the physics involved. The student makes some statement(s) which is/are relevant to the situation, showing that the problem is understood. | | |

| Question | | | Answer | Max mark |
|---|---|---|---|---|
| | | | **3 marks:** The maximum available mark would be awarded to a student who has demonstrated a good understanding of the physics involved. The student shows a good comprehension of the physics of the situation and has provided a logically correct answer to the question posed. This type of response might include a statement of the principles involved, a relationship or an equation, and the application of these to respond to the problem. This does not mean the answer has to be what might be termed an "excellent" answer or a "complete" one. | |
| **14.** | (a) | (i) | Capacitor has low reactance/impedance for high frequencies (therefore more current (and power) will be delivered to the tweeter at high frequencies).   **1** | 1 |
| | | (ii) | Inductor has low reactance/impedance for low frequencies (therefore more current (and power) will be delivered to the woofer at low frequencies).   **1** | 1 |
| | (b) | | $X_L = 2\pi f L$   **1** <br> $8 \cdot 0 = 2 \times \pi \times 3 \cdot 0 \times 10^3 \times L$   **1** <br> $L = 4 \cdot 2 \times 10^{-4}$ H   **1** <br><br> Accept: 4, 4·24, 4·244 | 3 |

| Question | | | Answer | Max mark |
|---|---|---|---|---|
| | (c) | (i) | $\dfrac{dI}{dt} = 20 \cdot 0$   **1** <br> $E = -L\dfrac{dI}{dt}$   **1** <br> $-9 \cdot 0 = -L \times 20 \cdot 0$   **1** <br> $L = 0 \cdot 45$ H   **1** <br><br> Accept: $0 \cdot 5$, $0 \cdot 450$, $0 \cdot 4500$ | 4 |
| | | (ii) | large (back) EMF.   **1** | 1 |